STUDENT WORKBOOK

to

HAZARDOUS MATERIALS:
MANAGING THE INCIDENT,
3rd Edition

By JoAnne Hildebrand

Chester, Maryland 21619
1-800-603-7700, 410-604-2540 • FAX 410-604-2541
www.redhatpub.com

PRODUCED BY:

LIGHTWORKS PHOTOGRAPHY AND DESIGN
Chester, Maryland 21619

Executive Producer: George Dodson

Production Coordinator/Designer: Kathleen Lawyer, Lightworks Design

Cartoon Illustrations: Mat Brown

Editor: Mary Hogan Hearle

Third Edition

LIBRARY OF CONGRESS NUMBER: 2005901954

ALSO AVAILABLE: Instructor Program with Guide, PowerPoint® presentations and exercises, Field Operations Guide and dedicated Web site, 8stepprocess.com.

ISBN: 1-932235-07-8

Printed in the United States

CONTENTS

CHAPTER 1

The Hazardous Materials Management System 1

CHAPTER 2

Health and Safety 31

CHAPTER 3

Incident Command System 57

CHAPTER 4

The Eight Step Process©: An Overview 81

CHAPTER 5

Site Management 99

CHAPTER 6

Identify The Problem 121

CHAPTER 7

Hazard Assessment and Risk Evaluation 147

CHAPTER 8

Select Personal Protective Clothing 179

CHAPTER 9

Information Management and Resource Coordination 201

CHAPTER 10

Implementing Response Objectives 221

CHAPTER 11

Decontamination 251

CHAPTER 12

Terminate the Incident 275

About the author...

JoAnne Hildebrand is the Academic Director of Fire Science at University of Maryland University College (UMUC), holds the rank of Collegiate Associate Professor, and chairs the USFA National Fire Academy (NFA) Degrees-at-a-Distance Higher Education Consortium. She is the author of the *Instructor's Guide to Hazardous Materials, Managing the Incident* (1st and 2nd editions) and the *Student Workbook to Hazardous Materials: Managing the Incident,* 2nd. ed. She has also authored and taught a number of online courses at UMUC and has served on numerous Degrees-at-a-Distance Course Guide development teams at the National Fire Academy. She has taught, "Managerial Issues in Hazardous Materials," a 400-level course required for the major in fire science at UMUC, for more than 10 years using *Hazardous Materials: Managing the Incident* as the primary textbook.

JoAnne was a founding member of NFPA Technical Committee on Occupational Safety and Health (NFPA-1500) and served on the committee for nine years. As a consultant to her family business, she contributes to operational readiness reviews for emergency response teams and provides advice in emergency planning for industry and public safety.

JoAnne received her M.A. and B.A., *Magna cum laude,* with the University of Maryland at College Park. She is a recipient of the University of Maryland University College's 2000 Stanley J. Drazek Teaching Excellence Award.

INTRODUCTION

The purpose of the Student Workbook is to provide a structured and enjoyable approach to studying the subject of hazardous materials incident response and management as presented in the textbook, Hazardous Materials, Managing the Incident, 3rd edition, by G. Noll, M. Hildebrand, and J. Yvorra. The Workbook is particularly helpful to individuals who are preparing for a promotional examination based on the textbook, and for those who are attending a training class in order to qualify or requalify as a Hazardous Materials Technician or HazMat On-Scene Incident Commander as outlined in *OSHA 1910.120 (q)—Hazardous Waste Operations and Emergency Response,* and by the educational competencies referenced in NFPA 472—*Professional Competence of Responders to Hazardous Materials*.

College students who are enrolled in a course that assigns the textbook as required or recommended reading will also find this Workbook an excellent study supplement that will help ensure high scores on tests and assignments.

The Workbook is organized into 12 lessons, each corresponding to a chapter in the textbook and providing learning aids arranged in the following sections:

Chapter Orientation—This section is designed to familiarize you with the subjects being covered and to help you get a grasp of how the material is organized. The exercise helps you to: 1) relate the material to your past experience; 2) rank your overall level of interest in the material; 3) consider the relevancy of the material to your current or future situation; and 4) identify areas that will require more of your time or effort to study.

Learning Objectives—When reading an assigned chapter, many students don't pay attention to the objectives because they misunderstand the reason for them. The truth is, without objectives you would be left to figure out on your own what you were supposed to learn and what you were supposed to do with that new knowledge or skill. This could be so frustrating at times that you might say, "I've read the chapter, so now what?" Learning objectives are statements that tell you and the outside world what you are supposed to be able to do by the end of the lesson. Learning objectives also help provide "proof" that you have achieved the goals of the textbook. This section helps you focus on and think about the chapter objectives in terms of their relevancy and importance in helping you reach your goals. This section also clearly identifies those objectives in each chapter that directly address core competencies for Hazardous Materials Technician and HazMat On-Scene Incident Commander as outlined in *OSHA 1910.120 (q)—Hazardous Waste Operations and Emergency Response*, and the educational competencies referenced in *NFPA 472—Professional Competence of Responders to Hazardous Materials*.

Abbreviations and Acronyms—Abbreviations and acronyms are shortened forms of words or phrases, used in place of the whole. "Etc." is a common abbreviation of "et cetera." Acronyms are usually formed by stringing the initial letters of words in a phrase or title to make a new shorthand word. OSHA, for example, is an acronym for the Occupational Safety and Health Administration, an agency of the federal government. Every occupation or field has a specialized vocabulary of abbreviations and acronyms and the emergency response community is no exception . Because they are so commonly used within a profession, it is important that you become familiar with the meaning of unfamiliar abbreviations and acronyms. If you have to stop and look up an acronym every time you come across it in your readings, you will soon become discouraged and will stop reading. If your professor uses an abbreviation that you don't recognize, you will undoubtedly feel confused or even miss critical points in the lecture. Mike Callan, IFSTA Instructor of the Year (1989) relates a true story of a student who came up to him after a presentation to ask him what the "Ideal - L H" was. The student was unfamiliar with the abbreviation "IDLH," and didn't recognize it when it was spoken as the letters I.D.L.H. Given the serious nature of the subject matter taught that day, this student missed a great deal. This section of the Workbook helps you learn the abbreviations and acronyms used in each chapter.

Study Session Overview—This section of the Workbook guides you through the process of comprehending and understanding the material in each chapter, and presents exercises to test your recall with multiple-choice, true/false, matching, fill-in-the blank, and short-answer questions, similar to those you would find on a promotional examination, course quiz, or a standardized certification examination. An answer key with page numbers referenced to the textbook is provided.

Practice—This section of the lesson helps you achieve a deeper level of learning and retention that occurs when you have an opportunity to apply your knowledge or ask your own questions. The practice exercises are not complicated; however, some exercises involve using outside resource materials, taking field trips, or using the Internet.

Important Terminology—This section of the Workbooks helps you build your technical vocabulary. By learning important terminology, you will become less dependent of the glossary and will become a more effective communicator. You will also score higher on tests. Please note that not all chapters include a section on new terminology.

Study Group Activities—These activities are valuable learning tools for students who are able to meet in a study group, either face-to-face or by using online conferencing software. In addition to group activities, each chapter provides two real-world scenarios and a series of discussion questions sequentially arranged in an increasing level of complexity and abstraction. The first question is typically designed to help you apply basic "textbook" principles. Follow-up questions are designed to take the discussion beyond the basic technical issues and into the more difficult political, legal, and management related issues. Many of these questions require you to make a personal judgment call on how to handle the problem. The more abstract the line of questioning becomes, the wider the range of possible responses. In most cases there are no right or wrong answers, only defendable ones for the group to justify in a group format.

Summary and Review—This section provides questions that help you assess how well you have grasped the objectives of the chapter. If you have trouble answering any of the questions, you may need to review the material again. If you are enrolled in a formal training class or college course, you can ask your instructor or professor for additional help.

Self evaluation—This section provides an opportunity to reflect on how well you feel you have mastered the material overall. You are directed to review all your work in the lesson and focus on areas where you see the need for improvement.

Pat on the Back—You've worked hard. Congratulations are in order!

HOW TO USE THE STUDENT WORKBOOK

In order to use this Workbook most effectively, you will need a copy of the textbook, *Hazardous Materials, Managing the Incident, 3rd edition*, by G. Noll, M. Hildebrand, and J. Yvorra. The textbook is divided into 12 chapters with chapters 1-3 addressing preparing for the incident, and chapters 4–12 addressing how to respond safely to a hazardous materials incident. Chapters 5–12 dedicate one chapter to each of the steps in the Eight Step Process©, a systematic way of responding to a hazmat incident.

Although it is optional, you should also have a copy of the **Field Operations Guide** (FOG) by Armando Bevelacqua. The FOG includes detailed tactical checklists that follow the Eight Step Process, a section on identification and recognition of containers, data cards on the top 50 hazardous materials and CBRNE's, as well as a matrix of WMD and drug lab precursor chemicals. The FOG is designed to be used at the incident scene and classroom as a reference guide to strategic and tactical decision-making. To order the textbook or FOG, call Fire Protection Publications, 1-800-604-4055 or Red Hat Publishing, 1-800-603-7700.

Access to the Internet is desirable but not required to use this Workbook. Additional study aids can be found at http://www.8STEPPROCESS.COM.

Supplies that you may find helpful include a spiral or loose leaf notebook, colored pencils (for making charts and diagrams), highlighter markers, index cards (for notes as well as flashcards), and a few file folders.

Locate a place in which you will study. While we all know people who can study in their family room or fire station kitchen, we should realize that this kind of environment works against the serious student. Your time is valuable and tightly managed as it is. If your commitment to learning is genuine, find a private, quiet area where you can concentrate. Study at a desk and use good lighting. ALWAYS read with a pen or pencil in your hand, and jot down notes in the "notes column" of the textbook.

Many students find it helpful to devise a study schedule—a flexible but pre-determined set of times during the week that are devoted to studying. If you are studying the textbook on your own (self-study) or as a member of a study group, you can progress through each lesson sequentially at your own pace, or you can complete only those lessons of interest to you. Lesson 1 helps you learn the material in Chapter 1 of the textbook, Lesson 2 helps you learn the material in Chapter 2 of the textbook, and so forth. If you are a member of a formal training or college class that has a syllabus[1], you'll want to make sure your study schedule coincides with or matches the schedule your instructor has prepared. For instance, you'll want to complete assignments on time and be prepared for quizzes.

If you are using this workbook for self-study, a study schedule is particularly important. Unless you are very familiar with your own study skills and habits, keep in mind that you'll probably need make a few changes to your schedule by the end of the next two weeks. It's OK to adjust your schedule from time-to time. The key is to have a schedule and to stick to it.

You will need a certain amount of time to read. How fast you read and can digest what you are reading depends of what you already know about a subject area, how difficult the reading is in a particular section or chapter, and how thoroughly you need to understand what you are reading. You will also need time to complete the exercises in this Workbook, and if you are taking a class, you will need time to complete your instructor's assignments and to prepare for examinations.

Always begin each study session with the Workbook. It breaks the textbook into manageable pieces, and provides structure for progressive learning. Please write all your answers to items and assignments in the spaces provided.

GETTING STARTED

I'm sure you have noticed the same thing I noticed about the textbook: it has a lot of pages and that means a lot of reading! What's more, some of the reading is fairly technical. You may find yourself asking, "Is it really necessary to read everything with the same level of focus and comprehension?"

Who and where you are on your professional ladder will determine, in part, how much of the material in the text you need to be familiar with vs. how much you need to truly master. If you are using the text in a formal educational setting, such as a training academy or college class, you will be expected to learn what the institution or your instructor deems necessary.

As is the case with most endeavors, a good way to begin is to become acquainted with the textbook. As you have just read above, it is divided into two broad areas—preparing for the hazmat response and implementing the hazmat response. Chapters 1 through 3 address preparing for the incident. Topics include the development of a comprehensive system for managing the hazmat problem, health and safety issues and concerns, and the development and implementation of an emergency management organization. Chapters 4 through 12 pertain to implementing the hazmat response, beginning with an overview of the Eight Step Process© and subsequent chapters that cover each of the eight individual functions of the Eight Step Process©. The information contained within each of these chapters builds incrementally, in step-wise fashion. You will find your knowledge base expanding logically and in an exciting manner as you progress through each chapter.

> The Eight Step Process© establishes a management structure which fits any size or level of hazmat response; it provides an incident management framework with one specific goal—to maximize safety for emergency response personnel and the general public.

Before going on, take a leisurely 15-minute break to leaf through the entire textbook. When you are finished, respond to the following items:

1. What is your very first impression of the textbook?

2. What parts of the textbook captured your immediate attention?

3. The text uses cartoons, full color photographs, graphics, and a multitude of charts and tables to convey information. What is your first impression of the visuals?

4. Have you ever thought what it would be like to research and write a textbook like this one? Comments?

5. What are your main reasons for studying the textbook?

6. At the present time, what is your overall personal standard of learning performance? For instance, if tested and graded in a traditional sense, are you aiming to achieve a grade of A or B, or are you more interested in passing with a fairly mid-range level of understanding? Are you attempting to achieve professional competencies such as those described in NFPA-472?

Next, please read the Acknowledgments on page x carefully. What does third-party review mean to you? What do you notice about the reviewers' titles or organizations where they work? Do you recognize any of the reviewers? What does it mean to you that these people took the time to provide third-party review of the textbook?

Read the remembrance to Jim Yvorra on page xiii. We often think of Jim as a writer, an instructor, or a mentor to young firefighters, but you should know that Jim was a highly motivated student who sought and took advantage of opportunities to learn. He once told me that fire and emergency response was the only "Last Frontier" on earth. What do you suppose he meant by that?

O.T. and the Kid© are introduced on page xvi. You'll get to know them better as you progress through the textbook. Would your crew or colleagues think of you as an O.T. or a Kid?

Congratulations on completing your orientation to the textbook and this section of the Student Workbook. Please turn the page and begin Chapter 1.

[1] A syllabus is a calendar schedule prepared by your instructor that includes reading and written assignments, dates that assignments are due, and information about exams and grading.

CHAPTER 1
THE HAZARDOUS MATERIALS MANAGEMENT SYSTEM

CHAPTER ORIENTATION

Open the text to page 2. Take about 10 minutes to skim the chapter. Pay attention to the boldface subject headings. Read the titles to all the figures and note how they fit into the subject headings. Please read the introduction and summary sections carefully. When you have finished looking through Chapter 1, respond to the following items. Please use the textbook as you jot down your comments in the spaces provided below:

1. In your own words, what makes a "systems approach" to hazardous materials management so important?

2. Reflect on your current level of knowledge or background experience about the topics covered in Chapter 1. Where have you read about, learned about, or applied this knowledge in the past?

3. What sections or parts of Chapter 1 strike you as especially interesting?

4. What particular subjects in this chapter are important for a person in your position to master?

5. What do you predict will be the hardest things for you to learn in this chapter?

LEARNING OBJECTIVES

Turn to page 2 and examine the chapter objectives. When you have finished, respond to the following question:

1. Which objectives in Chapter 1 do you feel you can achieve right now, with a reasonable level of confidence?

As you read the sections of the chapter that deal with the objectives you have identified above, make sure your ideas or knowledge base match those of the authors. If not, you should examine how your current understanding of the material differs from that of the authors. Depending on the level at which you wish to master the subject, discrepancies will have to be rectified and gaps will need to be filled.

ABBREVIATIONS AND ACRONYMS

The following abbreviations and acronyms are used in Chapter 1:

ACP	Area Contingency Plan (p. 7)
ALS	Advanced Life Support (p. 18)
ANSI	American National Standards Institute (p. 18)
API	American Petroleum Institute (p. 18)
ASTM	American Society of Testing and Materials (p. 18)
BLS	Basic Life Support (p. 18)
CAA	Clean Air Act (p. 7, 13)
CEPPO	Chemical Emergency Preparedness and Prevention Office (p. 23, 24)
CERCLA	Comprehensive Environmental Response, Compensation and Liability Act (p. 4, 7)
CFR	Code of Federal Regulations (p. 4)
CGA	Compressed Gas Association (p.18, 24-25)
DOT	Department of Transportation (p. 4)
EHS	Extremely Hazardous Substance (p. 4)
EMS	Emergency Medical Services (p. 10)
EMT-B	Emergency Medical Technician—Basic (p. 28)
EMT-I	Emergency Medical Technician—Intermediate (p. 28)
EMT-P	Emergency Medical Technician—Paramedic (p. 28)
EOP	Emergency Operations Plan (p. 9, 10, 11, 13, 20, 23, 24, 31)
EPA	Environmental Protection Agency (p. 4)
EPCRA	Emergency Planning and Community Right-to-Know Act (p. 7, 13)
ERG	Emergency Response Guidebook (p. 9)
ERT	Emergency Response Team (p. 8, 32)
FAA	Federal Aviation Administration (p. 27)
FBI	Federal Bureau of Investigation (p. 14)
FEMA	Federal Emergency Management Agency (p. 13, 26, 29)
FRA	Federal Railroad Administration (p.27)
FMECA	Failure Modes, Effects, and Criticality Analysis (p. 23)
HAZCOM	Hazard Communication Regulations (p. 14)
HAZMAT	Hazardous Materials (throughout the Chapter, defined on p. 4)
HAZOP	Hazard and Operability Study (p. 23)
HAZWOPER	Hazardous Waste Operations and Emergency Response (p. 7, 8, 12)
HMRT	Hazardous Materials Response Team (p. 4, 10, 14, 28)
HMS	Office of Hazardous Materials Safety (DOT/RSPA) (p. 26)
HMT	Hazardous Materials Technician (p. 4, 10, 11, 16, 17, 28, 32)

IAEM	International Association of Emergency Managers (p. 13)
ICS	Incident Command System (p. 32)
ICP	Integrated Contingency Plan (p. 24)
IMS	Incident Management System (p. 8, 10, 11, 17)
LEPC	Local Emergency Planning Committee (p. 7, 12, 24)
MSDS	Material Safety Data Sheet (p. 13, 14)
NCP	National Contingency Plan (p. 14)
NFPA	National Fire Protection Association (p. 4, 6, 18)
NRC	National Response Center (p. 7, 26, 27, 29)
NRT	National Response Team (p. 13, 14, 26)
NTSB	National Transportation Safety Board (p. 5)
OHME	Office of Hazardous Materials Enforcement (DOT/RSPA) (p. 26)
OPA	Oil Pollution Act of 1990 (p. 7)
OPS	Office of Pipeline Safety (p. 26)
OSC	On-Scene Coordinator (p. 14)
OSHA	Occupational Safety and Health Administration (p. 4, 14)
PSM	Process Safety Management (p. 7, 13, 22, 23)
RCRA	Resource Conservation and Recovery Act (p. 4, 6)
RMP	Risk Management Plan (p. 13, 23)
RPM	Remedial Project Manager (p. 33)
RRT	Regional Response Team (p. 11, 14)
RSPA	Research and Special Programs Administration (DOT) (p. 26)
SARA	Superfund Amendments and Reauthorization Act of 1986 (p. 7, 23)
SEI	Safety Equipment Institute (p. 18)
SERC	State Emergency Response Commission (p. 7, 12, 24)
USCG	United States Coast Guard (p. 14, 27)
WMD	Weapons of Mass Destruction (p. 22)

Locate these abbreviations and acronyms in the textbook (page numbers provided above) and underline them. Read the paragraph in which they are used.

EXERCISE

For each of the following sentences, write in the correct abbreviation or acronym (from the list above) so that the sentence makes sense. Use each abbreviation or acronym only once:

1. Title 40 of the ______________ contains the environmental regulations.

2. In accordance with Title III of SARA, the ______________ appoints or approves the LEPC membership.

3. In addition to its formal responsibilities, the ______________ serves as a focal point in the community for information and discussions about hazardous substances, emergency planning, and health and environmental risks.

4. Much of the information first responders need to safely handle incidents involving hazardous materials is contained in the ____________.

5. Workplaces are required to have ______________ available for every single hazardous chemical or substance that an employee uses or encounters as a part of the job.

6. If the ___________ is not utilized for all routine emergencies, don't expect the organizational structure to function and adapt effectively, efficiently, and safely when a major emergency occurs.

7. The job of Hazardous Materials Specialists is to respond with and provide support to the ______________.

8. The risk management program regulation is similar in scope to the OSHA ______________ standard, with the primary focus being community safety as compared to employee safety.

ANSWER KEY

1. Title 40 of the CFR contains the environmental regulations.

2. In accordance with Title III of SARA, the SERC appoints (or "approves") the LEPC membership.

3. In addition to its formal responsibilities, the LEPC serves as a focal point in the community for information and discussions about hazardous substances, emergency planning, and health and environmental risks.

4. Much of the information first responders need to safely handle incidents involving hazardous materials is contained the ERG .

5. Workplaces are required to have MSDS available for every single hazardous chemical or substance that an employee uses or encounters as a part of the job.

6. If the ICS is not utilized for all routine emergencies, don't expect the organizational structure to function and adapt effectively, efficiently, and safely when a major emergency occurs.

7. The job of Hazardous Materials Specialists is to respond with and provide support to the HMT.

8. The risk management program regulation is similar in scope to the OSHA PSM standard, with the primary focus being community safety as compared to employee safety.

CROSSWORD: ORGANIZATION ABBREVIATIONS

Use the clues below to solve the crossword.

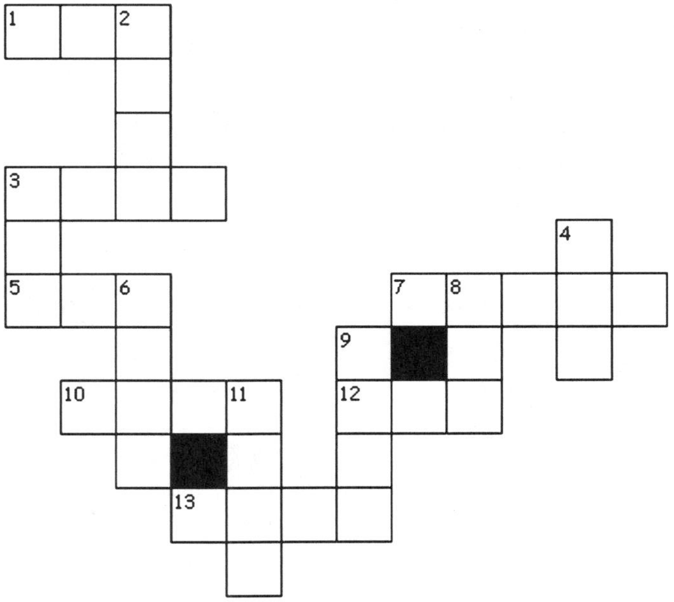

Across

1. This is one of ten agencies within the U.S. Department of Transportation concerned with intermodal transportation.
3. This agency conducts inspections and investigations to determine compliance with the Hazardous Materials Transportation Act.
5. This non-profit organization administers non-governmental, third-party certification programs to test and certify a broad range of safety and protective products.
7. This organization developed CAMEO ®, a system of software applications used widely to plan for and respond to chemical emergencies.
10. President Carter's 1979 executive order merged many of the separate disaster-related responsibilities into this federal organization.
12. You can download Airport Diagrams from this organization's website.
13. As part of a U.S. Department of Transportation (DOT) reorganization, this organization ceased operations on February 20, 2005.

Down

2. This organization provides an online directory of scientific and technical consultants and expert witnesses who perform consulting services or act as expert witnesses.
3. You can contact this federal organization to find out who is operating pipelines in your area.
4. This trade association has a number of committees dedicated to developing, revising, and approving consensus standards for the pipeline industry.
6. You would contact this organization to find out about the credential, "Certified Emergency Manager (CEM)".
8. Under the National Contingency Plan, this is the lead federal response agency for oil spills occurring in inland waters.
9. This organization developed a recommended practice for responding to hazardous materials incidents.
11. This organization serves as the coordinator of the U.S. voluntary standards system.

The Crossword Answer Key is at the end of this chapter.

STUDY SESSION OVERVIEW

Read pages 2 to the top of page 20, then take a short break to think about what you have read. Then read the rest of the chapter. Take margin notes as you go. Underline or highlight phrases that you feel are important.

When you have completed your reading, respond to the following questions. You may use the textbook to help you answer the questions, or work from memory.

1. How does Benner's definition of a hazardous material differ from the DOT definition?

2. In your own words, explain the difference between hazmat laws and hazmat regulations. Give an example of each.

3. Give an example of a hazmat-related voluntary consensus standard and explain briefly how it impacts your emergency service organization.

4. How could failure to comply with a standard of care create a legal problem for an emergency services organization?

5. Briefly describe a plausible scenario that would be considered a Level II Hazardous Materials Incident in your community.

6. In general terms, what safety issues are associated with clean-up operations?

SELF-TEST

Answer the following questions. You may use the textbook to help you answer the questions, or work from memory.

1. The following statements are all true, except one:
   [p. 4]
   a. Hazardous materials can be found virtually anywhere
   b. Hazardous materials can be used as a weapon for criminal or terrorist purposes
   c. All government agencies use the same standard definition of hazardous materials
   d. The DOT is one of several federal agencies that regulate hazardous materials

2. The term "dangerous goods" is most likely to be used in the context of:
   [p. 4]
   a. Workplace exposures
   b. Agricultural chemicals
   c. Interstate transportation
   d. International transportation

3. Which of the following regulatory system components is enacted through legislative action:
   [p. 6]
   a. Laws
   b. Regulations
   c. Rules
   d. Voluntary consensus standards

4. When a federal agency, state or municipal government adopts a consensus standard by reference, the document becomes a:
   [p. 6]
   a. Recommended practice
   b. Performance-based code
   c. Regulation
   d. Formal interpretation

5. Which of the following laws is known as the "Superfund" law:
   [p. 7]
   a. Oil Pollution Act of 1990
   b. The Clean Air Act
   c. The Resource Conservation and Recovery Act (1976)
   d. The Comprehensive Environmental Response Compensation and Liability Act (1980)

6. Hazardous Waste Operations and Emergency Response (29 CFR 1910.120), also known as HAZWOPER, is enforced in many states by:
   [p. 8]
   a. FEMA
   b. OSHA
   c. EPA
   d. DOT

7. HAZWOPER establishes requirements for all of the following, except one:
   [p. 8]
   a. Medical surveillance programs
   b. Emergency response procedures
   c. Single-point of contact reporting
   d. Post-emergency termination procedures

8. As identified within OSHA 1910.120(q)(6), the following responders are all trained to be capable of implementing the local Emergency Operations Plan, except one:
   [p. 12]
   a. Specialist Employees
   b. Hazardous Materials Technician
   c. Hazardous Materials Specialists
   d. On-Scene Incident Commander

9. Which of the following groups is responsible for developing and maintaining the state's emergency response plan:
   [p. 12]
   a. Regional Response Team
   b. Chemical Emergency Preparedness and Prevention Office
   c. Local Emergency Planning Committee
   d. State Emergency Response Commission

10. Which of the following groups is responsible for coordinating the Community Right-to-Know aspects of SARA, Title III:
   [p. 13]
   a. Local Emergency Planning Committee
   b. State Department of the Environment

c. Office of Hazardous Materials Safety
d. Chemical Emergency Preparedness and Prevention Office

11. Which of the following organizations assumes the role as federal On-Scene Coordinator (OSC) when the incident is a terrorism-related event:
    [p. 14]
    a. U.S. Coast Guard
    b. National Response Team
    c. Federal Bureau of Investigation
    d. Defense Threat Reduction Agency

12. Which of the following organizations develop voluntary consensus standards concerning hazardous materials:
    [p. 15, 18]
    a. National Fire Protection Agency (NFPA)
    b. Compressed Gas Association (CGA)
    c. American Petroleum Institute (API)
    d. All the above

13. There are four key elements in a hazardous materials management systems approach – 1) planning and preparedness; 2) prevention; 3) response; and:
    [p. 20]
    a. Inspection and enforcement
    b. Clean-up and recovery
    c. Critique
    d. Event tree analysis

14. Risk analysis assesses two considerations – 1) the probability or likelihood of an accidental release, and 2):
    [p. 22]
    a. The adequacy of response capabilities
    b. The size/extent of vulnerability zones
    c. The actual consequences that might occur
    d. The potential environmental impact

15. Both OSHA 1910.120 and NFPA 472 recommend that HMRT personnel be trained to:
    [p. 32]
    a. On-Scene Incident Commander level
    b. Hazardous Materials Specialist level
    c. Hazardous Materials Technician level
    d. First Responder at the Operations level

TRUE OR FALSE

16. True / False: Federal installations and military bases are exempt from EPA's right-to-know regulations. [p. 13]

17. True / False: Each of the 50 states and the U.S. territories maintains an enforcement agency that has responsibility for hazardous materials. [p. 14]

18. True / False: The purpose of NFPA 472 is to specify minimum competencies for those who will respond to hazardous materials incidents. [p. 16]

19. True / False: "Standard of Care" represents the minimum accepted level of hazardous materials emergency service that should be provided regardless of location or situation. [p. 19]

20. True / False: Almost all hazardous materials facilities, containers and processes are designed and constructed to some standard. [p. 24]

ANSWER KEY

Check your answers. If you missed more than five, you should read the chapter once again.

1. The following statements are all true, except one:
   [p. 4]
   a. Hazardous materials can be found virtually anywhere
   b. Hazardous materials can be used as a weapon for criminal or terrorist purposes
   c. All government agencies use the same standard definition of hazardous materials
   d. The DOT is one of several federal agencies that regulate hazardous materials

2. The term "dangerous goods" is most likely to be used in the context of:
   [p. 4]
   a. Workplace exposures
   b. Agricultural chemicals
   c. Interstate transportation
   d. International transportation

3. Which of the following regulatory system components is enacted through legislative action:
   [p. 6]
   a. Laws
   b. Regulations
   c. Rules
   d. Voluntary consensus standards

4. When a federal agency, state or municipal government adopts a consensus standard by reference, the document becomes a:
   [p. 6]
   a. Recommended practice
   b. Performance-based code
   c. Regulation
   d. Formal interpretation

5. Which of the following laws is known as the "Superfund" law:
[p. 7]
a. Oil Pollution Act of 1990
b. The Clean Air Act
c. The Resource Conservation and Recovery Act (1976)
d. The Comprehensive Environmental Response Compensation and Liability Act (1980)

6. Hazardous Waste Operations and Emergency Response (29 CFR 1910.120), also known as HAZWOPER, is enforced in many states by:
[p. 8]
a. FEMA
b. OSHA
c. EPA
d. DOT

7. HAZWOPER establishes requirements for all of the following, except one:
[p. 8]
a. Medical surveillance programs
b. Emergency response procedures
c. Single-point of contact reporting
d. Post-emergency termination procedures

8. As identified within OSHA 1910.120(q)(6), the following responders are all trained to be capable of implementing the local Emergency Operations Plan, except one:
[p. 12]
a. Specialist Employees
b. Hazardous Materials Technician
c. Hazardous Materials Specialists
d. On-Scene Incident Commander

9. Which of the following groups is responsible for developing and maintaining the state's emergency response plan:
[p. 12]
a. Regional Response Team
b. Chemical Emergency Preparedness and Prevention Office
c. Local Emergency Planning Committee
d. State Emergency Response Commission

10. Which of the following groups is responsible for coordinating the Community Right-to-Know aspects of SARA, Title III:
[p. 13]
a. Local Emergency Planning Committee
b. State Department of the Environment
c. Office of Hazardous Materials Safety
d. Chemical Emergency Preparedness and Prevention Office

11. Which of the following organizations assumes the role as federal On-Scene Coordinator (OSC) when the incident is a terrorism-related event:
[p. 14]
   a. U.S. Coast Guard
   b. National Response Team
   c. Federal Bureau of Investigation
   d. Defense Threat Reduction Agency

12. Which of the following organizations develop voluntary consensus standards concerning hazardous materials:
[p. 15, 18]
   a. National Fire Protection Agency (NFPA)
   b. Compressed Gas Association (CGA)
   c. American Petroleum Institute (API)
   d. All the above

13. There are four key elements in a hazardous materials management systems approach – 1) planning and preparedness; 2) prevention; 3) response; and:
[p. 20]
   a. Inspection and enforcement
   b. Clean-up and recovery
   c. Critique
   d. Event tree analysis

14. Risk analysis assesses two considerations – 1) the probability or likelihood of an accidental release, and 2):
[p. 22]
   a. The adequacy of response capabilities
   b. The size/extent of vulnerability zones
   c. The actual consequences that might occur
   d. The potential environmental impact

15. Both OSHA 1910.120 and NFPA 472 recommend that HMRT personnel be trained to:
[p. 32]
   a. On-Scene Incident Commander level
   b. Hazardous Materials Specialist level
   c. Hazardous Materials Technician level
   d. First Responder at the Operations level

TRUE OR FALSE:

16. True / **False**: Federal installations and military bases are exempt from EPA's right-to-know regulations. [p. 13]

17. **True** / False: Each of the 50 states and the U.S. territories maintains an enforcement agency that has responsibility for hazardous materials. [p. 14]

18. **True** / False: The purpose of NFPA 472 is to specify minimum competencies for those who will respond to hazardous materials incidents. [p. 16]

19. **True** / False: "Standard of Care" represents the minimum accepted level of hazardous materials emergency service that should be provided regardless of location or situation. [p. 19]

20. **True** / False: Almost all hazardous materials facilities, containers and processes are designed and constructed to some standard. [p. 24]

PRACTICE

1. Visit your LEPC Web site. Does it inform citizens in your county about how they can discover what chemical risks are present in their community?

2. Conduct an informal survey of your co-workers about "standard of care" and what it means to them and the organization. Do your findings identify any misunderstandings about the concept in relation to the discussion provided on page 19 in the text?

3. Read NFPA 472, *Professional Competence of Responders to Hazardous Materials Incidents.* This document can be ordered from the National Fire Protection Association or can be accessed free-of-charge for online review (see www.nfpa.org or visit http://www.8stepprocess.com for additional information.) Based on the standard, make a list of what a First Responder-Awareness level can do at an incident, what a First Responder-Operations can do, and what a Hazard Materials Technician can do.

4. Take the Emergency Management Institute's interactive web-based course, entitled IS-340 Hazardous Materials Prevention and Planning, located at http://training.fema.gov/EMIWeb/IS/is340.asp or by searching the EMI Web site. The course is free and takes about 4 hours to complete. Be sure to test your knowledge by taking the final examination. Jot down at least 3 things you learned in this course about hazmat emergency planning.

5. Go to http://www.8stepprocess.com for additional information and activities pertaining to Chapter 1, "The Hazardous Materials Management System".

IMPORTANT TERMINOLOGY

Following are important terms that you should know. Go to page 4 and review the definitions.

Hazardous materials (hazmats)
Hazardous substances
Extremely hazardous substances (EHSs)
Hazardous chemicals
Hazardous wastes
Dangerous goods

On the line next to each term in Column A, print the letter of its definition from Column B.

Column A Terminology	Column B Definitions
1.________Hazardous materials	A. Chemicals determined by the EPA to be extremely hazardous to a community during an emergency spill or release as a result of their toxicities and physical/chemical properties.
2.________Hazardous substances	B. In international transportation, the term used to refer to hazardous materials.
3.________Extremely hazardous substances (EHSs)	C. Any substance designated under the Clean Water Act and the Comprehensive Environmental Response, Compensation and Liability Act (CERCLA) as posing a threat to waterways and the environment when released.

4.________Hazardous chemicals

D. Any chemical that would be a risk to employees if exposed in the workplace.

5.________Hazardous wastes

E. Any substance or material in any form or quantity that poses an unreasonable risk to safety and health and property when transported in commerce.

6.________Dangerous goods

F. Discarded materials regulated by the EPA because of public health and safety concerns. Regulatory authority is granted under the Resource Conservation and Recovery Act (RCRA).

ANSWER KEY

Column A Terminology	Column B Definitions:
1.___E___Hazardous materials	A. Chemicals determined by the EPA to be extremely hazardous to a community during an emergency spill or release as a result of their toxicities and physical/chemical properties.
2.___C___Hazardous substances	B. In international transportation, the term used to refer to hazardous materials.
3.___A___Extremely hazardous substances (EHSs)	C. Any substance designated under the Clean Water Act and the Comprehensive Environmental Response, Compensation and Liability Act (CERCLA) as posing a threat to waterways and the environment when released.
4.___D___Hazardous chemicals	D. Any chemical that would be a risk to employees if exposed in the workplace.
5.___F___Hazardous wastes	E. Any substance or material in any form or quantity that poses an unreasonable risk to safety and health and property when transported in commerce.
6.___B___Dangerous goods	F. Discarded materials regulated by the EPA because of public health and safety concerns. Regulatory authority is granted under the Resource Conservation and Recovery Act (RCRA).

STUDY GROUP ACTIVITY

This activity is a "scavenger hunt" exercise to help you learn more about the NFPA and its voluntary consensus standards process while honing your internet search skills.

Directions: Divide into two or more teams, or work individually. Access the NFPA Web site at www.nfpa.org to answer the questions below. The first team or individual to answer all questions correctly wins.

1. What is the name of the NFPA's free newsletter that provides detailed information on NFPA codes and standards activities?

2. Who is eligible to submit a proposal to NFPA for a new safety-related project?

3. How many individuals are appointed to the Standards Council and who appoints them?

4. Which NFPA Committee is responsible for NFPA 472 Professional Competence of Responders to Hazardous Materials Incidents?

5. How many Committee member classifications are there?

6. Which Committee members may have an alternate member?

7. All NFPA consensus codes and standards are developed under the procedures of another well-known standards organization. Which one?

8. Several major conferences are hosted annually by NFPA. At which one is a technical committee report session held that offers members an opportunity to vote on NFPA code and standard actions, and also offers the public the opportunity to voice its opinions on those actions? During which month is it held?

9. There are approximately 77,000 members in the NFPA. Most members are in which professional field: fire service, electrical services, government, or insurance?

10. The NFPA has a "Student Member" membership category. What are the criteria for becoming a student member? Can student members vote?

11. The NFPA provides an educational grant for hazardous materials response teams. What is the name of the grant, for what amount is each grant, who can apply, and what must the grant be used for?

12. In what ways (identify two) does the 2002 edition NFPA 472 Standard for Professional Competence of Responders to Hazardous Materials Incidents differ from the previous edition? What has been added?

13. In what chapter of the 2002 edition of NFPA 472 are the competencies of "hazardous materials technician" covered?

The Answer Key is found at the end of this chapter.

STUDY GROUP LEARNING THROUGH INQUIRY SCENARIO 1-1

You are the Emergency Response Coordinator for an agricultural chemical manufacturing facility. Your company recently hired a new Safety Manager who is a Certified Safety Professional (CSP), but doesn't have any background in emergency response.

During the initial meeting with your new boss, she explains that she recently attended a national conference which conducted a simulated court case. Involved in the case was an emergency response organization which received an OSHA citation for its failure to have proper hazmat training and adequate site safety procedures. Because of what she learned at the conference, she is concerned that the plant is not in total compliance with the OSHA 29 CFR 1910.120 requirements. (See page 8, Chapter 1 for background information on CFR 1910.120.)

Your Supervisor requests a briefing on the plant's hazmat response and training program. As part of the briefing, you outline the following points:

- The Emergency Response Team (ERT) is an integrated unit that responds to fires, hazmat spills and basic medical emergencies.
- All of your ERT members are currently trained to the HAZWOPER First Responder Operations level.
- There is no formal Hazardous Materials Response Team (HMRT) on the complex because you rely on the local fire department which does have an HMRT. (If you are unfamiliar with the concept of an HMRT, review the material on page 31, Chapter-1.
- ERT members are trained to the Advanced Exterior Firefighting level, as identified in *NFPA 600—Industrial Fire Brigades*. The plant manufactures pesticides and the most significant fire problems involve flammable and combustible liquids, and flammable gases.
- Your command officers have not received any training beyond the First Responder Operations level and an 8-hour Incident Command Course provided by an outside contractor.
- The ERT does not have a formal Safety Officer.

Using the background information provided and the information discussed in Chapter 1, answer the following questions:

1) Based on your understanding of 29 CFR 1910.120 (HAZWOPER), is your Emergency Response Team (ERT) in compliance? If you believe it is in compliance, support your position using the material provided in Chapter 1.

2) If you are uncertain whether your ERT is in compliance with 29 CFR 1910.120, how would you determine that it is? Explain the basic plan that you would develop for determining that you are in compliance.

3) If your chemical plant were inspected by OSHA, do you think the company would be issued a citation? If you believe so, do you think it would be issued based on your current level of ERT training and level of OSHA compliance under 29 CFR 1910.120? If so, why?

4) Assume that some managers are not in compliance with the Incident Commander training requirements. How would you then handle this situation: your new Supervisor has vaguely suggested that you modify certain training records so that they are in compliance. In other words, the suggestion is that you knowingly falsify the training records. If you answered that you would refuse, would you do it if you were verbally ordered to do it? Would you do it under the same circumstances if you had one year to go before retirement? What if you were up for a promotion one year before retirement and the increase in salary would raise your pension?

STUDY GROUP LEARNING THROUGH INQUIRY SCENARIO 1-2

You were the Incident Commander at a multiple alarm warehouse fire that occurred three years ago in your community. The warehouse stored a wide range of petroleum-based paints and paint thinners. You made the decision to attack and extinguish the fire; however, the plan failed due to inadequate water supply. Unfortunately, there was significant runoff and pollution associated with this incident, and several nearby drinking water wells were contaminated as a result of the runoff.

The affected residents have joined in a class action lawsuit against your organization. One of the elements of the complaint is that you acted irresponsibly by attempting to extinguish the fire. The plaintiff's attorney has taken a deposition from an expert who has stated that a fire of this type should have been handled as a controlled burn. In other words, the expert is saying that you made the wrong decision.

Your organization's attorney informs you that an important element in the case will involve a concept known as the "Standard of Care." He warns you that you will have to give a deposition. You will probably be asked many difficult questions concerning whether you and your organization meet the minimum level of accepted hazmat service expected for an emergency response organization of similar size. The attorney representing the residents will attempt to show that: 1) you made the wrong decision, and 2) that you and your organization violated a Standard of Care. If the term Standard of Care is unfamiliar, you should review page 19 in Chapter 1 before answering the following questions.

Using the background information provided and the information discussed in Chapter 1, answer the following questions:

1) As an Incident Commander, how do you personally define the Standard of Care for an emergency response organization? List the primary standards, laws, or regulations that you feel you will be measured against to establish the minimum Standard of Care.

2) Using your own definition of a Standard of Care, do you feel that a "career," or fully paid, emergency response organization should be held to a higher Standard of Care than an all-volunteer organization? (For example, a career fire department versus a volunteer fire department.) If you answered the question no, why should a volunteer be held to more or less of a standard than a career individual or organization? What standard determines whether an individual is a "professional"?

3) Should an organized Hazardous Materials Response Team as defined by 29 CFR 1910.120 be held to a higher Standard of Care than a multipurpose emergency response organization (e.g., fire department engine company which meets NFPA 1001 or an industrial fire brigade which meets NFPA 600)?

SUMMARY AND REVIEW

1. Identify the primary target audience of the textbook.

2. True / False: The scope of the textbook is such that readers must have advanced-level training in chemistry.

3. EHS is an abbreviation for:

4. What is the U.S. Department of Transportation's (DOT) definition of hazardous materials?

5. Voluntary consensus standards are normally developed through:

   a. Municipal government
   b. Trade associations
   c. Local emergency planning committees
   d. Congress

6. CERCLA—The Comprehensive Environmental Response, Compensation and Liability Act (1980), also known as Superfund, requires those individuals responsible for the release of a hazardous material (commonly referred to as the responsible party) above a specified "reportable quantity" to notify the:

   a. National Response Center (NRC)
   b. State Emergency Response Commission
   c. Occupational Safety and Health Administration (OSHA)
   d. Office of Hazardous Materials Enforcement

7. SARA Title III is also known as the:

   a. Oil Pollution Act
   b. Clean Air Act
   c. Federal Water Pollution Control Act.
   d. Emergency Planning and Community Right-to-Know Act (EPCRA)

8. Hazardous Waste Operations and Emergency Response (29 CFR 1910.120), also known as HAZWOPER, establishes important requirements for both industry and public safety organizations that respond to hazmat or hazardous waste emergencies. Requirements cover the following areas:

   - Hazmat Emergency Response Plan
   - Emergency Response Procedures, including the establishment of an Incident Management System (IMS), the use of a buddy system with back-up personnel, and the establishment of a Safety Officer
   - Specific training requirements covering instructors and both initial and refresher training

   There are two other requirements. Identify one.

9. According to the specific levels of competency and associated training requirements identified within OSHA 1910.120(q)(6), First Responder–Operations personnel shall have sufficient training or experience to demonstrate objectively all of the following competencies, except one:

   a. Capability of implementing the local Emergency Operations Plan
   b. An understanding of basic hazardous materials terms.
   c. Knowledge of how to implement basic decontamination measures
   d. Knowledge of basic hazard and risk assessment techniques

10. Among the membership of Local Emergency Planning Committees (LEPC) are representatives from the following groups:

   - Elected state and local officials
   - Fire Department
   - Law Enforcement

   Identify three other groups:

11. The Local Emergency Planning Committee (LEPC) is responsible for all of the following, except one:

    a. Develop, regularly test, and exercise the Hazmat Emergency Operations Plan
    b. Manage the state's hazardous materials inspection and enforcement program within the community
    c. Receive and manage hazmat facility reporting information
    d. Conduct a hazards analysis of hazmat facilities and transportation corridors

12. When the National Response Team or Regional Response Team is activated for a federal response to an oil spill, hazmat, or terrorism event, a federal On-Scene Coordinator (OSC) will be designated to coordinate the overall response. For hazmat incidents, the On-Scene Coordinator will represent either EPA or the ______________ based upon the location of the incident:

    a. Department of Transportation (DOT)
    b. U.S. Coast Guard (USCG)
    c. Federal Bureau of Investigation (FBI)
    d. National Transportation Safety Board (NTSB)

13. The purpose of ______________ is to outline the minimum requirements that should be considered when dealing with responses to hazardous materials incidents and to specify operating guidelines:

    a. NFPA 471
    b. NFPA 472
    c. NFPA 1991
    d. NFPA 1994

14. NFPA 472 defines three levels of:

    a. Hazardous materials technician
    b. Incident Commander
    c. Private sector specialist employee
    d. Hazardous materials branch officer

15. Standard of Care is established by:

    - Existing laws and regulations
    - Voluntary consensus standards and recommended practices

    Standard of Care is also influenced by:

16. Identify the four key elements in a hazardous materials management systems approach:

17. There are four components of a hazards analysis program:

    1) Hazards identification
    2) Vulnerability analysis
    3) ____________________
    4) Emergency response resources evolution

18. Readers desiring further information on the integrated contingency plan (ICP) concept should contact the:

    a. Chlorine Institute
    b. EPA Chemical Emergency Preparedness and Prevention Office (CEPPO)
    c. Occupational Safety and Health Administration (OSHA)
    d. National Response Center (NRC)

19. Clean-up and recovery operations are designed to (1) clean up/remove the hazmat spill or release, and (2):

SUMMARY AND REVIEW ANSWERS

1. The primary target audience includes Hazardous Materials Technicians, the Hazmat Group Supervisor or Branch Director, the On-Scene Incident Commander, and members of organized hazardous materials response teams (HMRTs). Other special operations teams, such as Bomb Squads and Confined Space Rescue Teams, will also find specific chapters of interest.

   For your answer to be correct, it should include at least three of the audiences identified above (p. 4)

2. False (p. 4)

3. EHS is an abbreviation for Extremely Hazardous Substance (p. 2)

4. Hazardous materials—Any substance or material in any form or quantity that poses an unreasonable risk to safety and health and property when transported in commerce (Source: U.S. Department of Transportation [DOT], 49 Code of Federal Regulations (CFR) 171). (p. 4)

5. b. Trade associations (p. 6)

6. a. National Response Center (NRC) (p. 7)

7. d. Emergency Planning and Community Right-to-Know Act (EPCRA) (p. 7)

8. To be correct, your answer must include one of the following:

   - Medical Surveillance Programs
   - Postemergency termination procedures (p. 8)

9. a. Capability of implementing the local Emergency Operations Plan (p.9-10)

10. To be correct, your answer must include three of the following:

    - Emergency management
    - Public health officials
    - Hospital
    - Industry personnel, including facilities and carriers
    - Media
    - Community organizations (p. 12)

11. b. Manage the state's hazardous materials inspection and enforcement program within the community (p. 13)

12. b. U.S. Coast Guard (USCG) (p.14)

13. a. NFPA 471 (p. 15)

14. c. Private sector specialist employee (p.16)

15. To be correct, your answer must include at least one of the following:

    - Legal findings
    - Case law precedents (p. 19)

16. 1. Planning and preparedness

    2. Prevention

    3. Response

    4. Clean-up and recovery (p. 20)

17. 3) Risk analysis (p. 22)

18. b. EPA Chemical Emergency Preparedness and Prevention Office (CEPPO) (p. 24)

19. Restore the facility and/or community back to normal as soon as possible (p. 32)

Crossword Answer Key:

Across

1. FRA
3. OHME
5. SEI
7. CEPPO
10. FEMA
12. FAA
13. RSPA

Down

2. ASTM
3. OPS
4. API
6. IAEM
8. EPA
9. NFPA
11. ANSI

Study Group Scavenger Hunt Answer Key:

1. What is the name of the NFPA's free newsletter that provides detailed information on NFPA codes and standards activities?

   Answer: NFPA News.

2. Who is eligible to submit a proposal to NFPA for a new safety related project?

   Answer: Anyone.

3. How many individuals are appointed to the Standards Council and who appoints them?

   Answer: There are 13 individuals appointed by the NFPA Board of Directors.

4. Which NFPA Committee is responsible for NFPA 472 Professional Competence of Responders to Hazardous Materials Incidents?

   Answer: Hazardous Materials Response Personnel.

5. How many Committee member classifications are there?

   Answer: 8

6. Which Committee members may have an alternate member?

   Answer: Any Member except an alternate Member or Member Emeritus may have an alternate.

7. All NFPA consensus codes and standards are developed under the procedures of another well-known standards organization. Which one?

   Answer: The American National Standards Institute (ANSI).

8. Several major conferences are hosted annually by NFPA. At which is a technical committee report session held that offers members an opportunity to vote on NFPA code and standard actions, and also offers the public the opportunity to voice its opinions on those actions? During which month is it held?

   Answer: NFPA World Safety Conference and Exposition®, held in June.

9. There are approximately 77,000 members in the NFPA. Most members are in which professional field: fire service, electrical services, government, or insurance?

   Answer: Fire service.

10. The NFPA has a "Student Member" membership category. What are the criteria for becoming a student member? Can student members vote?

    Answer: To join as a Student Member you must be enrolled as a full-time student in a fire science or fire-related curriculum. Student Members cannot vote.

11. The NFPA provides an educational grant for hazardous materials response teams. What is the name of the grant, for what amount is each grant, who can apply, and what must the grant be used for?

    Answer: Warren E. Isman Educational Grant is for $5,000 to enable a hazardous materials response team to register for specialized training at a national hazmat conference. Any established hazardous materials response team from a fire or police department, or other public-funded program, can apply.

12. In what ways (identify two) does the 2002 edition *NFPA 472 Standard for Professional Competence of Responders to Hazardous Materials Incidents* differ from the previous edition? What has been added?

    Answer: The 2002 edition adds new coverage of weapons of mass destruction and contains material on responding to transportation or other incidents involving radioactive materials.

13. In what chapter of the 2002 edition of NFPA 472 are the competencies of "hazardous materials technician," covered?

    Answer: Chapter 6.

SELF EVALUATION

Please review all your work in this lesson. Now that you have completed this lesson, please review all your work and take about 15 minutes to note your stronger and weaker areas.

Overall I feel I did (very well / well / fair / not so well) on the acronyms and abbreviations exercise and crossword puzzle.

Overall I feel I did (very well / well / fair / not so well) on the self-test questions.

Overall I feel did (very well / well / fair / not so well) on the terminology (matching) exercise.

Overall I feel I did (very well / well / fair / not so well) on the summary and review questions.

List two areas in Chapter 1 in which you feel you could improve your skill or knowledge level:

1.

2.

Consider the following self-evaluation questions as they pertain to Chapter 1:

Am I taking effective margin notes?

Am I dedicating enough quality time to my studies?

Is anything distracting my focus?

Was any part of Chapter 1 too advanced for me?

Did I find that I don't have enough background experience to sufficiently grasp certain subject areas?

For areas in which I did particularly well, was it because I'm particularly interested in that subject matter? How so?

Were some things easier to learn because I have prior experience in learning or working with the concepts or principles?

Did I find that certain portions of the textbook seem to be better organized and effective in explaining key points?

What other students have had to say about Chapter 1 material:

"As a responder and a first-line supervisor, the next call out the door may be in response to a hazardous materials incident. Even though higher ranking staff and command officers may be on the way, the initial company officer is still expected to set up command and at a minimum establish defensive measures. Many of the "upwardly mobile" professionals in the fire service yearn for the day that they will be the chief responding on incidents that involve hazmats, so skills that are learned today in classes such as this one can be utilized while effectively mitigating the emergency."

I find it difficult to assimilate the mass of information and regulations issued by the various federal, state, and other stakeholders with a standing. There are so many little items that are critical but are buried under mounds of words.

Keeping a handle on all the legislation affecting hazmat response is difficult. The law is expansive and dry to read, yet it is so important. In my role in my department I'm not tasked with trying to keep up-to-date with that stuff so I don't look at it much unless I am taking a class on it. Scary thought.

I have a hard time with memorizing the different applicable codes and standards. I need to have a reference available for me for most of these. I know some people who can rattle these things off the top of their head; however, I do not have that kind of memory. I can, however, remember the ones I use consistently."

Pat on the Back

Congratulations on working through Chapter 1 in the textbook and for completing the exercises in this lesson.

CHAPTER 2
HEALTH AND SAFETY

CHAPTER ORIENTATION

Open the text to page 38. Take about 10 minutes to skim the chapter. Pay attention to the boldface subject headings. Read the titles to all the figures and note how they fit into the subject headings. Scan the case studies. Please read the introduction and summary sections carefully. When you have finished looking through Chapter 2, respond to the following items. Please use the textbook as you jot down your comments in the spaces provided below:

1. In your own words, describe what makes learning about the relationship of toxicity and exposure so important?

2. Reflect on your current level of knowledge or background experience about the topics covered in Chapter 2. Where have you read about, learned about, or applied this knowledge in the past?

3. What sections or parts of Chapter 2 strike you as especially interesting?

4. What particular subjects in this chapter are important for a person in your position to master?

5. What do you predict will be the hardest things for you to learn in this chapter?

LEARNING OBJECTIVES

Turn to page 38 and examine the chapter objectives. When you have finished, respond to the following question:

1. Which objectives in Chapter 2 do you feel you can achieve right now, with a reasonable level of confidence?

Highlight or place a check mark next to those objectives on pages 38-39 that address educational competencies referenced in *NFPA 472—Professional Competence of Responders to Hazardous Materials.*

As you read the sections of the chapter that deal with the objectives you have identified above, make sure your ideas or knowledge base match those of the authors. If not, you should examine how your current understanding of the material differs from that of the authors. Depending on the level at which you wish to master the subject, discrepancies will have to be rectified and gaps will need to be filled.

ABBREVIATIONS AND ACRONYMS

Following are the abbreviations and acronyms used in Chapter 2:

ACGIH	American Conference of Governmental Industrial Hygienists (p. 50)
AEGL	Acute Emergency Exposure Guidelines (p. 51)
AIHA	American Industrial Hygiene Association (p. 48, 51)
ALARA	As Low as Reasonably Achievable (p. 59)
BP	Blood pressure (p. 81, 82)
Bq	Becquerel (p. 60)
C	Centigrade (p. 62, 66, 67)
CGy	Centi-gray (p. 60)
Ci	Curie (p. 60)
CNS	Central Nervous System (p. 45, 46)
CPC	Chemical Protective Clothing (p. 61, 65, 66, 83)
DBA	Decibels on the AWeighted Scale (p. 68)
DoD	Department of Defense (p. 59)
dps	Disintegrations per Second (p. 60)
EKG	Electro-Cardiogram (p. 70, 81, 82)
ERPG	Emergency Response Planning Guideline (p. 51, 52, 55)
F	Fahrenheit (p. 62, 66, 67, 81)
Gy	Gray (p. 60)
IARC	International Agency for Research on Cancer (p. 58)
IDLH	Immediately Dangerous to Life or Health (p. 40, 51, 52, 53, 54, 55, 56, 57, 58, 79)
kg	Kilogram (p. 47, 48, 49)
l	Liter (p. 48)
Lb	Pounds (p. 47, 49)
LC	Lethal Concentration (p. 48, 53, 54)
LD	Lethal Dose (p. 44, 47, 49)
LOC	Level of Concern (p. 51, 52)
m3	Cubic Meter (p. 48, 50, 51)
μg	Microgram (p. 48)
mg	Milligram (p. 47, 48, 49, 50, 51)
mm Hg	Millimeters of Mercury (p. 81)

Mrem	Millirem (p. 38)
MSv	Milli-Sievert (p. 60)
NIOSH	National Institute of Occupational Safety and Health (p. 50, 52, 54, 57)
NTP	National Toxicology Program (p. 58)
PCB	Polychlorinated Biphenyls (p. 47)
PEL	Permissible Exposure Limit (p. 50, 52, 53, 54, 56)
ppb	Parts per Billion (p. 48, 49)
PPE	Personal Protective Equipment (p. 43, 55, 56, 64, 70, 74, 75)
ppm	Parts per Million (p. 48, 49, 50, 51, 53, 54, 55)
R	Roentgen (p. 60)
RAD	Radiation Absorbed Dose (p. 60)
Rehab	Rehabilitation Sector (p. 82)
REL	Recommended Exposure Levels (p. 50, 52)
rem	Roentgen Equivalent Man (p. 60)
SAR	Supplied Air Respirator (p. 56)
SI	International System Units (p. 59, 60)
SOP	Standard Operating Procedures(p. 72, 75, 76)
STEL	Short-Term Exposure Limit (p. 50, 53, 54)
Sv	Sievert (p. 60)
TLV	Threshold Limit Value (p. 44, 50, 51, 52, 53, 54, 55, 56, 58)
TLV/C	Threshold Limit Value/Ceiling (p. 50)
TLV/STEL	Threshold Limit Value/Short-Term Exposure Limit (p. 50)
TLV/TWA	Threshold Limit Value/Time-Weighted Average (p. 50, 51, 55, 56)

Locate these abbreviations and acronyms in the textbook (page numbers provided above) and underline them. Read the paragraphs in which they are used.

EXERCISE

For each of the following sentences, write in the correct abbreviation or acronym (from the list above) so that the sentence makes sense.

1. One ____________ of water weights exactly 1 kg.

2. There are some chemicals that cannot be excreted from the body, such as hydrogen fluoride,

which accumulates in the bones, and ____________, which accumulates in body fat.

3. There are two units of measurement commonly used for determining the relative toxicity of a chemical substance or compound: lethal dose (LD) and ____________.

4. The "Journal of Occupational and Environmental Hygiene" is the official journal of the American Industrial Hygiene Association and the ____________.

5. The audience was surprised to learn that responders wearing ______ are more likely to be injured by heat stress than by a chemical exposure.

6. At an ambient temperature of 18 degrees ____, people are usually unwilling to participate in decon showering because of the perception of discomfort.

7. Strengths of radioactive sources are measured in the SI unit Bq; however, the unit ____________ is still used in medical and technical practices.

8. The NFPA recommends that ____________ should be used in conjunction with other protective methods, such as medical monitoring and environmental surveillance.

9. Currently, _____________ is based on the assumption that any exposure to ionizing radiation carries with it some risk.

10. OSHA regulations require that hearing protection be provided whenever noise levels exceed 85 ________.

11. ______ is the federal agency responsible for conducting research and making recommendations for the prevention of work-related injury and illness.

12. One of its principal tasks of the ________ is to recommend TLVs for workplace exposure to chemicals.

13. The abbreviation for Electro-Cardiogram is ________.

14. The abbreviation for Sievert is ________.

15. The abbreviation for Millimeters of Mercury is ________.

ANSWER KEY

1. One L of water weights exactly 1 kg.
2. There are some chemicals that cannot be excreted from the body, such as hydrogen fluoride, which accumulates in the bones, and PCBs, which accumulate in body fat.
3. There are two units of measurement commonly used for determining the relative toxicity of a chemical substance or compound: lethal dose (LD) and LC.
4. The "Journal of Occupational and Environmental Hygiene" is the official journal of the American Industrial Hygiene Association and the ACGIH.
5. The audience was surprised to learn that responders wearing CPC are more likely to be injured by heat stress than by a chemical exposure.
6. At an ambient temperature of 18 degrees C, people are usually unwilling to participate in decon showering because of the perception of discomfort.
7. Strengths of radioactive sources are measured in the SI unit Bq; however, the unit Ci is still used in medical and technical practices.
8. The NFPA recommends that PPE should be used in conjunction with other protective methods, such as medical monitoring and environmental surveillance.
9. Currently, ALARA is based on the assumption that any exposure to ionizing radiation carries with it some risk.
10. OSHA regulations require that hearing protection be provided whenever noise levels exceed 85 dBA.
11. NIOSH is the federal agency responsible for conducting research and making recommendations for the prevention of work-related injury and illness.
12. One of the principal tasks of the ACGIH is to recommend TLVs for workplace exposure to chemicals.
13. The abbreviation for Electro-Cardiogram is EKG.
14. The abbreviation for Sievert is Sv.
15. The abbreviation for Millimeters of Mercury is mm Hg.

STUDY SESSION OVERVIEW

Read pages 38 to the top of page 68, then take a short break to think about what you have read. Read the rest of the chapter. Take margin notes as you go. Underline or highlight phrases that you feel are important.

When you have completed your reading, respond to the following questions. You may use the textbook to help you answer, or work from memory.

1. Figure 2.3 on page 44 illustrates the dose/response relationship of a commonly used substance, alcohol. The effect of consuming bourbon on the body is a function of the dose. Using the template below, substitute another common substance for bourbon and indicate the acute and chronic effects as related to dose. (Examples: sunlight, cigarette smoke, coffee)

Dose	Acute Effect	Chronic Effect

3. In your own words, explain the difference between a "local effect" and a "systemic effect" of a hazmat exposure. Give an example of each.

4. How can you estimate the IDLH of a toxic chemical if you know its TLV/TWA?

5. Which of the following IDLH atmospheres is the easiest to deal with using personal protective equipment: toxic, flammable, or oxygen deficient?

6. In your own words, explain time, distance, and shielding as they relate to exposure to radioactive materials.

7. What conditions promote or have an effect on heat stress?

8. Under what conditions can the ABC's of emergency treatment be administered to a contaminated victim (a victim who has not been decontaminated)?

9. Describe an ideal area in which to situate a rehabilitation area.

SELF-TEST

Answer the following questions. You may use the textbook to help you answer, or work from memory.

1. Exposure + _________ equals Health Hazard:
   [p. 41]
   a. Concentration
   b. Dose
   c. Toxicity
   d. Chemical agent

2. Absorption through the ________ is one of the fastest means of exposure:
   [p. 43]
   a. Eyes
   b. Palms and fingertips
   c. Knees and elbows
   d. Forearms

3. The target organ of hepatotoxins is:
   [p. 45]
   a. Kidneys
   b. Liver
   c. Bones
   d. Blood system

4. Lead and organophosphate pesticides are examples of:
[p. 45]
a. Nephrotoxins
b. Hematotoxins
c. Teratogens
d. Neurotoxins

5. Dose = Concentration + __________:
[p. 47]
a. Time
b. Toxicity
c. Effect
d. Rate of absorption

6. Which of the following is a measurement commonly cited for determining the relative toxicity of a chemical?
[p. 47]
a. pH
b. PEL
c. LD_{50}
d. ppm

7. Which of the following is a physical indicator of likely IDLH conditions?
[p. 56]
a. Visible vapor cloud
b. Confined spaces
c. Dead birds or discolored foliage
d. All of the above

8. Which of the following is an example of ionizing radiation?
[p. 58]
a. Microwaves
b. Lasers
c. X-rays
d. Infrared waves

9. In the U.S., radioactive materials dose limits for workers performing emergency services are provided in:
[p. 60]
a. Ci
b. rem
c. Gy
d. Sv

10. The following are all symptoms of heat stroke, except one:
[p. 62]
a. Dry, hot skin
b. Muscle cramps
c. Weakness
d. Full rapid pulse

11. Wet clothing extracts heat from the body up to _____ faster than dry clothing.
[p. 66]
   a. 5 times
   b. 20 times
   c. 50 times
   d. 240 times

12. Excessive noise levels can have the following effect:
[p. 68]
   a. Personnel being annoyed, startled, or distracted
   b. Physical damage to ears, pain, and temporary and/or permanent hearing loss
   c. Interference with communications, which may limit the ability of ERP to warn of danger or enforce proper safety precautions
   d. All of the above

13. There are five components of a medical surveillance program for hazmat responders, including pre-employment screening, periodic medical examination, emergency treatment, record-keeping and review, and:
[p. 69]
   a. Non-emergency treatment
   b. Physician referral
   c. Physical fitness program
   d. Wellness program

14. Which of the following is an advantage of using operational checklists to meet the site safety requirements?
[p. 76]
   a. Ability to ensure that specific organizational guidelines and SOPs are followed.
   b. Ability to track activities and performance.
   c. Ability to document the plan of action and decision-making process.
   d. All of the above.

15. Post-entry medical monitoring is performed:
[p. 82]
   a. Before leaving the Hot Zone
   b. Following decontamination
   c. During debriefing
   d. Within 24 hours of entry

16. The Rehabilitation Area should be located:
[p. 83]
   a. Near the Incident Command Post to facilitate communications
   b. In the staging area where it is easily accessible by EMS units
   c. In the warm zone to facilitate prompt reentry following rehab
   d. In a location that provides physical rest by allowing the body to recuperate from the hazards and demands of the emergency

TRUE OR FALSE

17. True / False: [p. 42] Skin absorption can occur with no sensation to the skin itself.

18. True / False: [p. 52] The lower the reported concentration, the more toxic the material.

19. True / False: [p. 59] Personal protective clothing provides moderate protection against gamma radiation.

20. True / False: [p. 78] Both the Incident Safety Officer and the Hazmat Group Safety Officer must have authority to stop any operations that are deemed unsafe.

ANSWER KEY

Check your answers. If you missed more than five, you should read the chapter once again.

1. Exposure + ____________equals Health Hazard:
   [p. 43]
   a. Concentration
   b. Dose
   c. Toxicity
   d. Chemical agent

2. Absorption through the ________ is one of the fastest means of exposure:
   [p. 43]
   a. Eyes
   b. Palms and fingertips
   c. Toxicity
   d. Chemical agent

3. The target organ of hepatotoxins is:
   [p. 45]
   a. Kidneys.
   b. Liver.
   c. Bones.
   d. Blood system.

4. Lead and organophosphate pesticides are examples of:
   [p. 45]
   a. Nephrotoxins.
   b. Hematotoxins.
   c. Teratogens.
   d. Neurotoxins.

5. Dose = Concentration + __________:
[p. 47]
a. Time
b. Toxicity
c. Effect
d. Rate of absorption

6. Which of the following is a measurement commonly cited for determining the relative toxicity of a chemical?
[p. 47]
a. pH
b. PEL
c. LD_{50}
d. ppm

7. Which of the following is a physical indicator of likely IDLH conditions?
[p. 56]
a. Visible vapor cloud
b. Confined spaces
c. Dead birds or discolored foliage
d. All of the above

8. Which of the following is an example of ionizing radiation?
[p. 58]
a. Microwaves
b. Lasers
c. X-rays
d. Infrared waves

9. In the U.S., radioactive materials dose limits for workers performing emergency services are provided in:
[p. 60]
a. Ci
b. rem
c. Gy
d. Sv

10. The following are all symptoms of heat stroke, except one:
[p. 62]
a. Dry, hot skin
b. Muscle cramps
c. Weakness
d. Full rapid pulse

11. Wet clothing extracts heat from the body up to _____ faster than dry clothing:
[p. 66]
a. 5 times
b. 20 times
c. 50 times
d. 240 times

12. Excessive noise levels can have the following effect:
    [p. 68]
    a. Personnel being annoyed, startled, or distracted.
    b. Physical damage to ears, pain, and temporary and/or permanent hearing loss.
    c. Interference with communications, which may limit the ability of ERP to warn of danger or enforce proper safety precautions.
    d. All of the above.

13. There are five components of a medical surveillance program for hazmat responders, including pre-employment screening, periodic medical examination, emergency treatment, recordkeeping and review, and:
    [p. 69]
    a. Non-emergency treatment
    b. Physician referral
    c. Physical fitness program
    d. Wellness program

14. Which of the following is an advantage of using operational checklists to meet the site safety requirements?
    [p. 76]
    a. Ability to ensure that specific organizational guidelines and SOPs are followed.
    b. Ability to track activities and performance.
    c. Ability to document the plan of action and decision-making process.
    d. All of the above

15. Post-entry medical monitoring is performed:
    [p. 82]
    a. Before leaving the Hot Zone
    b. Following decontamination
    c. During debriefing
    d. Within 24 hours of entry

16. The Rehabilitation Area should be located:
    [p. 83]
    a. Near the Command Post to facilitate communications.
    b. In the staging area where it is easily accessible by EMS units.
    c. In the warm zone to facilitate prompt reentry following rehab.
    d. In a location that provides physical rest by allowing the body to recuperate from the hazards and demands of the emergency

TRUE OR FALSE:

17. **True** / False: Skin absorption can occur with no sensation to the skin itself.
    [p. 42]

18. **True** / False: The lower the reported concentration, the more toxic the material.
    [p. 52]

19. True / **False**: Personal protective clothing provides moderate protection against gamma radiation.
[p. 59]

20. **True** / False: Both the Incident Safety Officer and the Hazmat Group Safety Officer must have authority to stop any operations that are deemed unsafe.
[p. 78]

PRACTICE

1. The human body can be subject to seven types of harm events, listed below and discussed on pages 45-46. Using the Internet and other sources, locate actual events in which an emergency responder was harmed by each type, and briefly describe the circumstances.

   Thermal:

   Mechanical:

   Poisonous:

   Corrosive:

Asphyxiation:

Radiation:

Etiological:

2. Review the poison lines presented on pages 53-54 in the textbook. Sketch a poison line for hydrogen sulfide (H_2S). You will need to consult outside resource materials, such as MSDSs for H_2S to complete this exercise.

3. Compare your department's procedures for preventing or reducing heat stress to those listed on page 65. Are there any procedures listed there that are not practiced in your department? Should they be added? Do you have suggestions for adding to the list on page 65?

4. Using outside reference materials, including the EPA and AIHA websites, fill in the values for the following three hazardous chemicals:

Chemical	ERGP-2	1/10 IDLH	IDLH	TLV/TWA	TLV/STEL
Ammonia					
Chlorine					
Sulfur Dioxide					

	AEGL-2					
Chemical	5 min.	10 min.	30 min.	60 min.	4 hr.	8 hr.
Ammonia						
Chlorine						
Sulfur Dioxide						

5. Go to http://www.8stepprocess.com for additional information and activities pertaining to Chapter 2 "Health and Safety."

IMPORTANT TERMINOLOGY

The following are all the important terms that you should know. Locate these terms in Chapter 2 and/or the Glossary and review the definitions.

Parts per Million (ppm)

Parts per Billion (ppb)

Lethal Dose (LD50)

Lethal Concentration (LC50)

Permissible Exposure Limit (PEL)

Threshold Limit Value/Time-Weighted Average (TLV/TWA)

Threshold Limit Value/Ceiling (TLV/C)

Threshold Limit Value/Short-Term Exposure Limit (TLV/STEL)

Immediately Dangerous to Life or Health (IDLH)

Emergency Response Planning Guideline (ERPG)
Acute Exposure Guideline Levels (AEGL)
Radiation Absorbed Dose (RAD or rad)
Roentgen equivalent Man (Rem); Millierem (mrem)
Roentgen

On the line next to each term in Column A, print the letter of its definition from Column B.

Column A Terminology	**Column B Definitions:**
1.______Parts per Million (ppm)	A. An atmospheric concentration of any toxic, corrosive, or asphyxiant substance that poses an immediate threat to life, or would cause irreversible or delayed adverse health effects, or would interfere with an individual's ability to escape from a dangerous atmosphere.
2.______Parts per Billion (ppb)	B. The concentration of an inhaled substance that results in the death of 50% of the test population in a specific time period (usually 1 hour).
3.______Lethal Dose (LD50)	C. Numerically equivalent to 0.000,001 (10^{-6})
4.______Lethal Concentration (LC50)	D. The 15-minute, time-weighted average exposure that should not be exceeded at any time, nor repeated more than four times daily with a 60-minute rest period required between each STEL exposure.
5.______Permissible Exposure Limit (PEL)	E. The maximum concentration that should not be exceeded, even instantaneously.
6.______Threshold Limit Value/Time-Weighted Average (TLV/TWA)	F. Numerically equivalent to 0.000,000,001 (10^{-9})
7.______Threshold Limit Value/Ceiling (TLV/C)	G. The maximum airborne concentration below which it is believed that nearly all individuals could be exposed for up to one hour without experiencing or developing irreversible or serious health effects or symptoms which could impair an individual's ability to take protective action.
8.______Threshold Limit Value/Short-Term Exposure Limit (TLV/STEL)	H. The maximum time-weighted concentration at which 95% of exposed, healthy adults suffer no adverse effects over a 40-hour work week.
9.______Immediately Dangerous to Life or Health (IDLH)	I. Developed by the National Research Council's Committee on Toxicology to provide uniform exposure guidelines for the general public.

10._____Emergency Response Planning Guideline (ERPG-2)

11._____Acute Exposure Guideline Levels (AEGL)

12._____Radiation Absorbed Dose (RAD or rad)

13._____Roentgen equivalent Man (Rem)

14._____Roentgen

J. Unit for radiation dose

K. The unit of dose equivalent; takes into account the effectiveness of different types of radiation.

L. A measure of the charge produced in air created by ionizing radiation, usually in reference to gamma radiation.

M. The concentration of an ingested, absorbed, or injected substance which results in the death of 50% of the test population.

N. The maximum airborne concentration of a material to which an average healthy person may be exposed repeatedly for 8 hours each day, 40 hours per week without suffering adverse effects.

ANSWER KEY

Column A Terminology

1. <u>C</u> Parts per Million (ppm)
2. <u>F</u> Parts per Billion (ppb)
3. <u>M</u> Lethal Dose (LD50)
4. <u>B</u> Lethal Concentration (LC50)
5. <u>H</u> Permissible Exposure Limit (PEL)
6. <u>N</u> Threshold Limit Value/ Time-Weighted Average (TLV/TWA)

Column B Definitions:

A. An atmospheric concentration of any toxic, corrosive, or asphyxiant substance that poses an immediate threat to life, or would cause irreversible or delayed adverse health effects, or would interfere with an individual's ability to escape from a dangerous atmosphere.

B. The concentration of an inhaled substance that results in the death of 50% of the test population in a specific time period (usually 1 hour).

C. Numerically equivalent to 0.000,001 (10^{-6})

D. The 15-minute, time-weighted average exposure that should not be exceeded at any time, nor repeated more than four times daily with a 60-minute rest period required between each STEL exposure.

E. The maximum concentration that should not be exceeded, even instantaneously.

F. Numerically equivalent to 0.000,000,001 (10^{-9})

7.__E__Threshold Limit Value/Ceiling (TLV/C)

8.__D__Threshold Limit Value/Short-Term Exposure Limit (TLV/STEL)

9.__A__Immediately Dangerous to Life or Health (IDLH)

10.__G__Emergency Response Planning Guideline (ERPG)

11.__I__Acute Exposure Guideline Levels

12.__J__Radiation Absorbed Dose (RAD or rad)

13.__K__Roentgen equivalent Man (Rem)

14.__L__Roentgen

G. The maximum airborne concentration below which it is believed that nearly all individuals could be exposed for up to one hour without experiencing or developing irreversible or serious health effects or symptoms which could impair an individual's ability to take protective action.

H. The maximum time-weighted concentration at which 95% of exposed, healthy adults suffer no adverse effects over a 40-hour work week.

I. Developed by the National Research Council's Committee on Toxicology to provide uniform exposure guidelines for the general public.

J. Unit for radiation dose

K. The unit of dose equivalent; takes into account the effectiveness of different types of radiation.

L. A measure of the charge produced in air created by ionizing radiation, usually in reference to gamma radiation.

M. The concentration of an ingested, absorbed, or injected substance which results in the death of 50% of the test population.

N. The maximum airborne concentration of a material to which an average healthy person may be exposed repeatedly for 8 hours each day, 40 hours per week without suffering adverse effects.

STUDY GROUP ACTIVITY

1. As a group, examine and debate the "safety truths" presented on pages 75-76 in the textbook.

STUDY GROUP LEARNING THROUGH INQUIRY SCENARIO 2-1

You are the Health and Safety Supervisor of a large chemical manufacturing plant with 1,500 employees. You have been assigned the task of developing a Medical Surveillance Program for the members of the plant's Emergency Response Team (ERT). Facility hazards include flammable liquids and gases, corrosives, and poisonous liquids.

The volunteer ERT is trained to the Hazardous Materials Technician level, and includes personnel from the Operations, Maintenance, Safety, and Administration Departments within the chemical plant's work force. In addition, there are two Maintenance Department members on each shift who are also trained to the Hazmat Technician level.

Given the information provided in Chapter 2, what would you recommend as the components of the Medical Surveillance Program? (See page 68, Chapter 2 for details on Medical Surveillance Programs.) Management has also asked for your recommendations on several specific issues:

1) What criteria should be used for initial entry and re-entry medical monitoring?

2) Since medical emergencies are handled by the off-site fire department, how can medical monitoring operations be performed?

3) Should the facility contact the local hospital? If yes, what type of information should be exchanged?

4) Several managers have stated that physical examinations can be provided on a 3-year interval. Do you agree or disagree with this statement? What is your response?

STUDY GROUP LEARNING THROUGH INQUIRY SCENARIO 2-2

You are the supervisor of a Hazardous Materials Response Team (HMRT) for a metropolitan fire department. One of your HMRT members informs you that she is pregnant and wants to continue working as long as possible up until the time that she will go on light-duty status. However, she questions you concerning the HMRT's policy regarding potential exposure to embryotoxins. Specifically, she wants your advice concerning how long it would be safe to work on the HMRT while pregnant. Your department's Policy and Procedures Manual provides clear guidance for firefighters but does not address the issue of HMRT members.

After discussing the issue with the employee, you raise the issue with your Fire Chief. The Chief agrees that a policy should be developed and asks you to consult with the department's Medical Officer. The Chief wants you to address the following questions in a briefing paper for a future staff meeting. Use information provided in Chapter 2 to develop your own opinion. Also consult Chapter 7, page 518 for more information regarding embryotoxins.

1) From a fire department policy perspective, should HMRT members be placed in a greater risk category than the average firefighter? The Chief agrees that firefighters are in a high risk occupation as compared to other occupations, but considering the special equipment, training and procedures the HMRT uses, are they really at greater chronic health risk than any other employee who is not on the HMRT?

2) If you believe that the health risks of HMRT members are greater than those of the average firefighter, what key points will you work into the briefing paper the Chief has requested? How will you support your case? (Review pages 41 and 42, Chapter 2.)

3) If HMRT members are really in a high-risk occupation, are female HMRT members exposed to an even greater risk while they are pregnant? Why? Why not?

SUMMARY AND REVIEW

1. What is the health hazard equation?

2. Identify the five routes of exposure:

3. Exposure to various types and doses of hazmats over a period of years is associated with chronic health effects. Identify at least two ways to monitor such exposures.

4. Identify three ways in which the human eye can be exposed via skin absorption:

5. What is the dose equation?

6. When evaluating the establishment of hazard control zones at hazmat emergencies, which of the following are generally the most informative: TLV, IDLH, ERPG, AEGL or 1/10th the IDLH?

7. Carcinogens do not have an IDLH value, and many do not have a TLV value. Why?

8. List the four types of ionizing radiation:

9. Although sometimes found at remediation operations, air-cooled jackets and suits are typically not used for emergency response applications. Why?

10. The following statements about ice-cooled vests are all true, except one:

   a. Ice-cooled vests are a passive cooling system that operates on the principle of conductive heat cooling.
   b. Ice-cooled vests are relatively inexpensive and lightweight.
   c. Ice-cooled vests are not as effective as air-cooled units and water-cooled jackets.
   d. These vests can also be used with heat packs for operations in extremely cold working environments.

11. What steps can be taken to prevent or minimize injuries from cold exposures?

12. There are two primary objectives of a medical surveillance program. The first is to determine that an individual can perform his or her assigned duties, including the use of personal protective clothing and equipment. What is the other objective?

13. What is the purpose of including nonemergency treatment in a medical surveillance program?

14. Identify at least three elements of a personal protective equipment program (PPE).

15. Identify at least three components of a site safety plan.

16. Identify at least three topics that should be covered in a pre-entry safety briefing.

17. The following are all objectives of medical monitoring, except one:

   a. Obtain baseline vital signs.
   b. Identify and preclude from participation individuals who are at increased risk to sustain either injury or illness.
   c. Facilitate the early recognition and treatment of personnel with adverse physiological and/or emotional responses.
   d. Advise entry personnel and the IC of any unsafe practices or conditions.

SUMMARY AND REVIEW ANSWERS

1. Exposure + Toxicity = Health Hazard.(p. 41)
2. Inhalation, skin absorption, ingestion, direct contact, and injection .(p. 42)
3. To monitor such exposures, responders should be provided with baseline medical profiles, participate in medical surveillance program, and document all exposures.

   For your answer to be correct, it should include at least two of the three methods identified above.(p. 42)
4. • Chemical splashed directly into the eye.

   • Chemical is carried on toxic smoke particles into the eyes from a fire.

   • Gases or vapors are absorbed through the eye.(p. 43)
5. Dose = Concentration x Time.(p. 41)
6. The various TLV and IDLH values are generally the most informative.(p. 52)
7. It is assumed that there is not threshold value below which these materials are "safe". (p. 58)
8. Alpha particles, beta particles, gamma rays, and neutron particles.(p. 58)
9. These units require an airline and large quantities of breathing air (10 to 25 cubic feet per minute) and are not as effective as the active and passive cooling units in controlling body core temperatures. (p. 64)
10. c. Ice-cooled vests are not as effective as air-cooled units and water-cooled jackets. (p. 64)
11. Ensure that all personnel are wearing appropriate clothing (preferably layered) and have warm shelters or vehicles available. (p. 66)
12. The second primary objective of a medical surveillance program is to detect any changes in body system functions caused by physical and/or chemical exposures. (p. 68)
13. The signs and symptoms of certain chemical exposures may not be present for 24 to 72 hours after exposure. This is particularly true when dealing with chemicals that have delayed effects. In many instances, those exposed may already be off duty and out of contact. Personnel operating at an incident should be medically evaluated before being released. In addition, the termination procedure should provide for a briefing for all ERP on the signs and symptoms of exposure, documentation and completion of health exposure logs or forms, postincident points of contact, and how to get immediate treatment if necessary. (p. 73)
14. For your answer to be correct, it should include at least three of the following:
    - Hazard assessment
    - Medical monitoring of personnel
    - Equipment selection and use
    - Training program
    - Inspection, maintenance, and storage program (p. 74)

15. Components of a site safety plan should include: site map or sketch, hazard and risk analysis of the identified hazardous materials, site monitoring, establishment of control zones, site safety practices and procedures, communications, implementation of an incident management organization and the location of the incident command post, decontamination practices, EMS support, and other relevant topics.

    For your answer to be correct, it should include at least three of the components identified above. (p. 74)

16. Topics should include objectives of the entry operation, a review of all assignments, verification of radio procedures (designated channels) and emergency signals (both hand signals and audible), emergency escape plans and procedures, protective clothing requirements, immediate signs and symptoms of exposure, and the location and layout of the decon area.

    For your answer to be correct, it should include at least three of the topics identified above. (p. 78)

17. d. Advise entry personnel and the IC of any unsafe practices or conditions (p. 81)

SELF EVALUATION

Now that you have completed this lesson, please review all your work and take about 15 minutes to note your stronger and weaker areas.

Overall I feel I did (very well / well / fair / not so well) on the acronyms and abbreviations exercise.

Overall I feel I did (very well / well / fair / not so well) on the self-test questions.

Overall I feel did (very well / well / fair / not so well) on the terminology (matching) exercise.

Overall I feel I did (very well / well / fair / not so well) on the summary and review questions.

When compared to the previous lesson, I think I performed (better / worse / equally well).

List two areas in Chapter 2 in which you feel you could improve your skill or knowledge level:

1.

2.

Consider the following self-evaluation questions as they pertain to Chapter 2:

Am I taking effective margin notes?

Am I dedicating enough quality time to my studies?

Is anything distracting my focus?

Was any part of Chapter 2 too advanced for me?

Did I find that I don't have enough background experience to sufficiently grasp certain subject areas?

For areas in which I did especially well, was it because I'm particularly interested in that subject matter? How so?

Were some things easier to learn because I have prior experience in learning or working with the concepts or principles?

Did I find that certain portions of the textbook seem to be better organized and effective in explaining key points?

What other students have had to say about Chapter 2 material:

> "As a firefighter, it is essential that I am aware of the relationship between exposure and toxicity. Without this knowledge, I am putting myself at great risk every time I respond to a hazmat incident. In addition, since I hope to eventually achieve a greater rank, I also need to be able to develop health and safety management programs. Without these skills, I will not be an effective leader."
>
> "In my opinion, the most important aspect of any hazmat response program is the health and safety management aspect. For obvious reasons, the health and safety of the responders and of the public we serve must be integral to all planning and response strategies. The old hazmat adage of "what happens if I do nothing?" at an incident really comes into play if injuries are probable with no measurable positive outcomes. No incident commander will send the troops into harm's way without reason. With thorough pre-planning keeping health and safety as priority #1, the IC will better understand the risks and rewards for given actions. Sometimes it is far better to protect the outer perimeter and let an incident "run out of steam" on its own."

Pat on the Back

Congratulations on working through Chapter 2 in the textbook and for completing the exercises in this lesson.

CHAPTER 3

INCIDENT COMMAND SYSTEM

CHAPTER ORIENTATION

Open the text to page 88. Take about 10 minutes to skim the chapter. Pay attention to the boldface subject headings. Read the titles to all the figures and note how they fit into the subject headings. Please read the introduction and summary sections carefully. When you have finished looking through Chapter 3, respond to the following items. Please use the textbook as you jot down your comments in the spaces provided below:

1. Federal regulations require that both public safety and industrial emergency response organizations use a nationally recognized incident command system for emergencies involving hazardous materials. But beyond regulatory requirements, why use ICS?

2. Reflect on your current level of knowledge or background experience about the topics covered in Chapter 3. Where have you read about, learned about, or applied this knowledge in the past?

3. What sections or parts of Chapter 3 strike you as looking especially interesting?

4. What particular subjects in this chapter are important for a person in your position to master?

5. What do you predict will be the hardest things for you to learn in this chapter?

LEARNING OBJECTIVES

Turn to page 88 and examine the chapter objectives. When you have finished, respond to the following question:

1. Which objectives in Chapter 3 do you feel you can achieve right now, with a reasonable level of confidence?

Highlight or place a check mark next to those objectives on pages 38-39 that addresses educational competencies referenced in *NFPA 472—Professional Competence of Responders to Hazardous Materials*.

As you read the sections of the chapter that deal with the objectives you have identified above, make sure your ideas or knowledge base match those of the authors. If not, you should examine how your current understanding of the material differs from that of the authors'. Depending on the level at which you wish to master the subject, discrepancies will have to be rectified and gaps will need to be filled.

ABBREVIATIONS AND ACRONYMS

The following abbreviations and acronyms are used in Chapter 3:

CHEMTREC	Chemical Transportation Emergency Response Center (p. 91, 121)
CRM	Crew Resource Management (p. 122, 123)
DECON	Decontamination (p. 98, 103, 109, 112, 113)

DEQ	Department of Environmental Quality (p. 107)
DHS	Department of Homeland Security (p. 126)
EOC	Emergency Operations Center (p. 91, 99, 104, 105, 108, 117)
EOD	Explosive Ordinance Disposal (p. 91)
ERP	Emergency Response Plan (p. 96, 104)
FAA	Federal Aviation Administration (p. 126)
IAP	Incident Action Plan (p. 88, 107, 111, 116, 117, 121, 124, 125)
ICP	Incident Command Post (p. 99, 102, 103, 104, 105, 108, 117)
ICS	Incident Command System (p. 89, 90, 91, 93, 96, 98, 99, 100, 102, 104, 106, 108, 109, 113, 115, 117, 118, 122, 123, 124, 125)
IMT	Incident Management Team (p. 124)
IST	Incident Support Team (p. 124)
LEPC	Local Emergency Planning Committee (p. 91, 105)
NIMS	National Incident Management System (p. 92, 93, 94)
NOAA	National Oceanic and Aeronautical Administration (p. 104, 105)
NOP	Next Operational Period (p. 100)
NRP	National Response Plan (p. 94, 95)
OIM	Off-Shore Installation Manager (p. 122)
PIO	Public Information Officer (p. 90, 103)
RIT	Rapid Intervention Team (p. 112)
SWAT	Special Weapons and Tactics (p. 91)
ROE	Rules of Engagement (p. 118)
UC	Unified Commanders (p. 89)
USAR	Urban Search and Rescue (p. 91)
WMD	Weapons of Mass Destruction (p. 108)

Locate these abbreviations and acronyms in the textbook (page numbers provided above) and underline them. Read the paragraph in which they are used. Then answer the questions below:

1. Which of the following would most likely have extensive knowledge of offshore legislation, drilling, production, maintenance, engineering and safety management:
   a. PIO
   b. RIT
   c. OIM
   d. IMT

2. Which of the following would most likely have the capacity to extract an entry team in the event of an emergency:
   a. UC
   b. RIT
   c. IST
   d. IMT

3. Which of the following is a member of the ICS Command Staff:
   a. UC
   b. PIO
   c. RIT
   d. IMT

4. Which of the following are deployed for the rescue of victims of structural collapse:
   a. SWAT
   b. LEPC
   c. IMT
   d. USAR

5. Which of the following would be most interested *primarily* in the environmental impact of a release:
   a. CHEMTREC
   b. DHS
   c. DEQ
   d. FAA

For each of the following sentences, write in the correct abbreviation or acronym (from the list above) so that that sentence makes sense. Use each abbreviation or acronym only once:

6. Operated by the American Chemistry Council, _______________ can provide information and technical assistance to emergency responders.

7. _______________ was originally defined in 1977 by aviation psychologist Dr. John Lauber as "…using all available resources (information, equipment and people) to achieve safe and efficient flight operations." Key components include command, leadership, and resource management.

8. OSHA 1910.120 defines _______________ as the removal of hazardous substances from employees and their equipment to the extent necessary to preclude foreseeable health effects.

9. The _______________ is a secured site where government or facility officials exercise centralized direction and control in an emergency.

10. The_______________ is a plan that establishes guidelines for handling hazmat incidents as required by regulations such as SARA, Title III and HAZWOPER (29 CFR 1910.120).

11. The _______________ consists of the strategic goals, tactical objectives and support requirements for the incident.

12. ______________ is an organized system of roles, responsibilities, and standard operating procedures used to manage and direct emergency operations.

13. The ______________ is appointed by a state emergency response commission, as required by SARA Title III, to formulate a comprehensive emergency plan for its corresponding local government or mutual aid region.

14. ______________ is a standardized systems approach to incident management that consists of five major sub-divisions collectively providing a total systems approach to all-risk incident management.

15. ______________ are Command level representatives from each of the primary responding agencies who present their agency's interests as a member of a unified command team.

16. The ______________ consolidates 22 agencies and 180,000 employees, unifying once-fragmented Federal functions in a single agency dedicated to protecting America from terrorism.

17. The ______________ provides a safe, secure, and efficient U.S. national airspace system

18. The ______________ is the location at which the primary command functions are executed, usually collocated with the incident base.

19. ______________ provides a national weather service.

20. The ______________ establishes a comprehensive all-hazards approach to enhance the ability of the United States to manage domestic incidents.

21. A ______________ team is a law enforcement tactical unit trained to deal with violent and dangerous situations

22. ______________ are designed to kill large numbers of people, typically targeting civilians and military personnel alike.

ANSWER KEY

1. Which of the following would most likely have extensive knowledge of offshore legislation, drilling, production, maintenance, engineering and safety management:
   a. PIO
   b. RIT
   c. OIM
   d. IMT

2. Which of the following would most likely have the capacity to extract an entry team in the event of an emergency:
   a. UC
   b. RIT
   c. IST
   d. IMT

3. Which of the following is a member of the ICS Command Staff:
   a. UC
   b. PIO
   c. RIT
   d. IMT

4. Which of the following are deployed for the rescue of victims of structural collapse:
   a. SWAT
   b. LEPC
   c. IMT
   d. USAR

5. Which of the following would be *most* interested primarily in the environmental impact of a release:
   a. CHEMTREC
   b. DHS
   c. DEQ
   d. FAA

6. Operated by the American Chemistry Council, CHEMTREC can provide information and technical assistance to emergency responders.

7. CRM was originally defined in 1977 by aviation psychologist Dr. John Lauber as "…using all available resources (information, equipment and people) to achieve safe and efficient flight operations." Key components include command, leadership, and resource management.

8. OSHA 1910.120 defines DECON as the removal of hazardous substances from employees and their equipment to the extent necessary to preclude foreseeable health effects.

9. The EOC is a secured site where government or facility officials exercise centralized direction and control in an emergency.

10. The ERP is a plan that establishes guidelines for handling hazmat incidents as required by regulations such as SARA, Title III and HAZWOPER (29 CFR 1910.120).

11. The IAP consists of the strategic goals, tactical objectives and support requirements for the incident.

12. ICS is an organized system of roles, responsibilities, and standard operating procedures used to manage and direct emergency operations.

13. The LEPC is appointed by a state emergency response commission, as required by SARA Title III, to formulate a comprehensive emergency plan for its corresponding local government or mutual aid region.

14. NIMS is a standardized systems approach to incident management that consists of five major sub-divisions collectively providing a total systems approach to all-risk incident management.

15. UCs are Command level representatives from each of the primary responding agencies who present their agency's interests as a member of a unified command team.

16. The DHS consolidates 22 agencies and 180,000 employees, unifying once-fragmented Federal functions in a single agency dedicated to protecting America from terrorism

17. The FAA provides a safe, secure, and efficient U.S. national airspace system

18. The ICP is the location at which the primary command functions are executed, usually collocated with the incident base.

19. NOAA provides a national weather service.

20. The NRP establishes a comprehensive all-hazards approach to enhance the ability of the United States to manage domestic incidents.

21. A SWAT team is a law enforcement tactical unit trained to deal with violent and dangerous situations

22. WMD are designed to kill large numbers of people, typically targeting civilians and military personnel alike.

STUDY SESSION OVERVIEW

Read pages 88 to the middle of page 106, then take a short break to think about what you have read. Then read the rest of the chapter. Take margin notes as you go. Underline or highlight phrases that you feel are important.

When you have completed your reading, respond to the following questions. You may use the textbook to help you answer the questions, or work from memory.

1. What roles do police officers and law enforcement play in the ICS organization?

2. Where would you go to locate technical information specialists?

3. The textbook differentiates between an incident and a crisis (see page 95). Give an example of an incident that happened in your community and briefly note how this incident could have transitioned to a crisis situation.

3. Review the resource management lessons presented on page 108. Which one really stands out as true in your experience? In what way?

4. What does "Command presence" mean to you?

5. From your experience, what factors contribute to the "reluctance of on-scene personnel to provide regular and timely updates to the ICP or EOC" (page 117).

6. The textbook states that an emergency can have a favorable technical or operational outcome and still be a political disaster. Briefly describe a hazmat emergency that you responded to or know about that resulted in substantial political problems, even though the overall outcome was operationally successful. What factors contributed to the political problems?

7. Briefly outline the "rule of threes" for minimizing political vulnerability. How could the rule of threes have helped to minimize the political problem(s) associated with the incident you described above in question #6.

SELF-TEST:

Answer the following questions. You may use the textbook to help you answer the questions, or work from memory.

Column A (below) lists the players and participants who will interact within the ICS organization. Using Chapter 3 and/or the glossary, match each player to its role in Column B:

(On the line next to each term in Column A, print the letter of its definition from Column B.)

Column A **Terminology**	**Column B** **Definitions:**
1._______Incident Commander	A. Crews of specially trained and medically evaluated individuals responsible for directly managing and controlling hazmat problems.
2._______Unified Commanders	B. Individuals who provide specific expertise to the IC either in person, by telephone, or through other means.
3._______Hazardous Materials Response Teams (HMRTs)	C. Organization legally responsible under government law for the clean-up of a hazmat release.
4._______Fire/EMS Companies	D. The individual responsible for establishing and managing the overall incident action plan (IAP).
5._______Police Officers and Law Enforcement Personnel	E. They receive "911" calls for assistance and dispatch Enforcement Personnel appropriate units to the incident locations.

6.______Emergency Response Teams (ERTs)	F. Crews of specially trained and medically evaluated individuals responsible for directly managing and controlling hazmat problems.
7. ______Special Operations Teams	G. Individuals who provide important support services at the incident (i.e., water and utility company employees, heavy equipment operators, etc.)
8.______Communications Personnel	H. Individuals who normally do not have an emergency response function but who bring a lot of political clout to the incident (i.e., mayors, city/county managers, etc.)
9.______Responsible Party	I. Crews of specially trained personnel used within business and industrial facilities for the control and mitigation of emergency situations.
10.______Facility Managers	J. Individuals who may provide both mitigation and support services at the incident (e.g., spill control, product transfer operations, site clean-up and recovery, etc.)
11.______Support Personnel	K. Individuals who are responsible for determining the origin and cause of the hazmat release, including any related evidence collection and preservation.
12.______Technical Information Specialists	L. Command-level representatives from each of the primary responding agencies who present their agency's interests as a member of a unified command organization.
13.______Environmental Clean-up Contractors	M. Individuals representing various elements of the media who work to inform the public of major happenings within their community or region.
14.______Government Officials	N. Resources for ensuring scene safety (i.e., scene and traffic control), perpetrator arrest or control, evidence preservation, etc.
15.______Investigators	O. Individuals who normally do not have an on-scene emergency response function, but who are key players within the plant environment.
16.______Hazardous Materials Response Teams (HMRTs	P. Provide resources for fire suppression, rescue, and medical triage, treatment and transport.
	Q. Highly trained and equipped response teams who deliver a highly specialized response service and capability (i.e., urban search and rescue (USAR) teams, bomb squads, etc.)

17. Which of the following requires that both public safety and industrial emergency response organizations use a nationally recognized Incident Command System for hazmat emergencies:
[p. 92]
   a. OSHA Directive Number 2/59A
   b. OSHA 1910.120(q)
   c. 40 CFR Part 68
   d. 29 CFR 1910.119

18. The National Incident Management System (NIMS) is a baseline incident management organization that is utilized by:
[p. 92]
   a. Federal government
   b. State and local governments
   c. Many private sector organizations
   d. All of the above

19. "Unity of command" means:
[p. 99]
   a. Work is assigned based on the functions to be performed
   b. Lines of authority are clearly defined
   c. Every person reports to only one supervisor
   d. No more than five individuals should report to any one supervisor

20. At the very least, a(n) ________ must be identified on all incidents, regardless of their size:
[p. 102]
   a. IC
   b. Safety Officer
   c. Liaison Officer
   d. Staging Officer

Column A (below) lists the four sections with ICS. Match each section to its respective primary responsibility in Column B:

Column A **ICS Section**	**Column B** **Responsibility**
21.______Operations Section	A. Conducts assessments and identifies the future needs and then develops the plans required to support the response.
22.______Planning Section	B. Responsible to get funds where they are needed.
23.______Logistics Section	C. Delivers the required tactical level services in the field to make the problem go away, including fire, hazmat, emergency medical, etc.
24.______Administration/Finance Section	D. Provides all incident support needs, including facilities, services, and materials.

25. The Safety Officer, Liaison Officer, and Information Officer all have the following in common:
[p. 101-102]
   a. They are all Command Staff officers
   b. They all report directly to the Hazmat Group Safety Officer
   c. They are all required by federal law to be staffed at all Level III hazmat incidents
   d. They all report to and operate from the Emergency Operations Center (EOC)

26. The Service Branch and the Support Branch are both elements of the:
[p. 103]
   a. Operations Section
   b. Planning Section
   c. Logistics Section
   d. Administration/Finance Section

27. Staging is an element within the:
[p. 103]
   a. Operations Section
   b. Planning Section
   c. Logistics Section
   d. Administration/Finance Section

28. Whenever a situation is encountered that could immediately cause or has caused injuries to emergency response personnel, the term ___________ should precede the radio transmission:
[p. 106]
   a. Safety alert
   b. Emergency traffic
   c. Distress hail
   d. Code Urgent

29. The Hazardous Materials Group Safety Officer is responsible for:
[p. 112]
   a. Establishing tactical objectives for the Hazardous Materials Entry Team
   b. Determining the appropriate level of decontamination to be provided
   c. Ensuring that health exposure logs and records are maintained for all Hazardous Materials Group personnel, as needed.
   d. Ensuring that all hot zone operations are coordinated with the Operations Section Chief or IC to ensure tactical goals are being met.

30. Which of the following is responsible for establishing a safe refuge area, when needed:
[p. 113]
   a. Back-up Team
   b. Decontamination Team
   c. Site Access Control Unit
   d. Hazardous Materials Medical Unit

ANSWER KEY

Check your answers. If you missed more than six, you should read the chapter once again.

Column A Terminology	**Column B Definitions:**
1. ___D___ Incident Commander (p. 89)	A. Crews of specially trained and medically evaluated individuals responsible for directly managing and controlling hazmat problems.
2. ___L___ Unified Commanders (p. 89)	B. Individuals who provide specific expertise to the IC either in person, by telephone, or through other means.
3. ___A___ Hazardous Materials Response Teams (HMRTs) (p. 90)	C. Organization legally responsible under government law for the clean-up of a hazmat release.
4. ___P___ Fire/EMS Companies (p. 90)	D. The individual responsible for establishing and managing the overall incident action plan (IAP).
5. ___N___ Police Officers and Law Enforcement Personnel (p. 90)	E. They receive "911" calls for assistance and dispatch Enforcement Personnel appropriate units to the incident locations.
6. ___I___ Emergency Response Teams (ERTs) (p. 90)	F. Crews of specially trained and medically evaluated individuals responsible for directly managing and controlling hazmat problems.
7. ___Q___ Special Operations Teams (p. 90–91)	G. Individuals who provide important support services at the incident (i.e., water and utility company employees, heavy equipment operators, etc.)
8. ___E___ Communications Personnel (p. 91)	H. Individuals who normally do not have an emergency response function but who bring a lot of political clout to the incident (i.e., mayors, city/county managers, etc.)
9. ___C___ Responsible Party (p. 91)	I. Crews of specially trained personnel used within business and industrial facilities for the control and mitigation of emergency situations.
10. ___O___ Facility Managers (p. 91)	J. Individuals who may provide both mitigation and support services at the incident (e.g., spill control, product transfer operations, site clean-up and recovery, etc.)
11. ___G___ Support Personnel (p. 91)	K. Individuals who are responsible for determining the origin and cause of the hazmat release, including any related evidence collection and preservation.

12.__B__Technical Information Specialists (p. 91)	L. Command-level representatives from each of the primary responding agencies who present their agency's interests as a member of a unified command organization.
13.__J__Environmental Clean-up Contractors (p. 91)	M. Individuals representing various elements of the media who work to inform the public of major happenings within their community or region.
14.__H__Government Officials (p. 91)	N. Resources for ensuring scene safety (i.e., scene and traffic control), perpetrator arrest or control, evidence preservation, etc.
15.__K__Investigators (p. 92)	O. Individuals who normally do not have an on-scene emergency response function, but who are key players within the plant environment.
16.__F__Hazardous Materials Response Teams (HMRTs (p. 90)	P. Provide resources for fire suppression, rescue, and medical triage, treatment and transport.
	Q. Highly trained and equipped response teams who deliver a highly specialized response service and capability (i.e., urban search and rescue (USAR) teams, bomb squads, etc.)

17. Which of the following requires that both public safety and industrial emergency response organizations use a nationally recognized Incident Command System for hazmat emergencies:
    [p. 92]
    a. OSHA Directive Number 2/59A
    b. OSHA 1910.120(q)
    c. 40 CFR Part 68
    d. 29 CFR 1910.119

18. The National Incident Management System (NIMS) is a baseline incident management organization that is utilized by:
    [p. 92]
    a. Federal government
    b. State and local governments
    c. Many private sector organizations
    d. All of the above

19. "Unity of command" means
    [p. 99]
    a. Work is assigned based on the functions to be performed
    b. Lines of authority are clearly defined
    c. Every person reports to only one supervisor
    d. No more than five individuals should report to any one supervisor

20. At the very least, a(n) _________ must be identified on all incidents, regardless of their size: [p. 102]
   a. **IC**
   b. Safety Officer
   c. Liaison Officer
   d. Staging Officer

Column A (below) lists the four sections with ICS. Match each section to its respective primary responsibility in Column B:

Column A ICS Section	Column B Responsibility
21.__C__Operations Section (p. 100)	A. Conducts assessments and identifies the future needs and then develops the plans required to support the response.
22.__A__Planning Section (p. 100)	B. Responsible to get funds where they are needed.
23.__D__Logistics Section (p. 100)	C. Delivers the required tactical level services in the field to make the problem go away, including fire, hazmat, emergency medical, etc.
24.__B__Administration/Finance Section (p. 101)	D. Provides all incident support needs, including facilities, services, and materials.

25. The Safety Officer, Liaison Officer, and Information Officer all have the following in common:
   [p. 101-102]
   a. **They are all Command Staff officers**
   b. They all report directly to the Hazmat Group Safety Officer
   c. They are all required by federal law to be staffed at all Level III hazmat incidents
   d. They all report to and operate from the Emergency Operations Center (EOC)

26. The Service Branch and the Support Branch are both elements of the:
   [p. 103]
   a. Operations Section
   b. Planning Section
   c. **Logistics Section**
   d. Administration/Finance Section

27. Staging is an element within the:
   [p. 103]
   a. **Operations Section**
   b. Planning Section
   c. Logistics Section
   d. Administration/Finance Section

28. Whenever a situation is encountered that could immediately cause or has caused injuries to emergency response personnel, the term __________ should precede the radio transmission:
   [p. 106]
   a. Safety alert
   b. **Emergency traffic**
   c. Distress hail
   d. Code Urgent

29. The Hazardous Materials Group Safety Officer is responsible for: [p. 112]
    a. Establishing tactical objectives for the Hazardous Materials Entry Team
    b. Determining the appropriate level of decontamination to be provided
    c. **Ensuring that health exposure logs and records are maintained for all Hazardous Materials Group personnel, as needed.**
    d. Ensuring that all hot zone operations are coordinated with the Operations Section Chief or IC to ensure tactical goals are being met.

30. Which of the following is responsible for establishing a safe refuge area, when needed: [p. 113]
    a. Back-up Team
    b. Decontamination Team
    c. **Site Access Control Unit**
    d. Hazardous Materials Medical Unit

PRACTICE

1. Locate the course entitled "IS 700—National Incident Management System (NIMS), An Introduction" on the FEMA website. (At the time of this writing, the URL is http://training.fema.gov/EMIWeb/IS/is700.asp.) This self-study course explains the purpose, principles, key components and benefits of NIMS. Work through the course by yourself or with a study partner. (This will take approximately 3 hours.) FEMA also offers a basic ICS course (IS 195) that you may wish to take first.
2. Starting with the equipment list provided on page 104, and using outside resources, including the Internet, develop a proposal to equip your department with a state-of-the art incident command post kit. You do not need to research costs, but you should be able to substantiate the need for the equipment or services you are proposing to acquire.
3. Develop a presentation that could be delivered to local officials that supports the need for an alternate EOC location. Use local examples to support your position, if possible.
4. Prepare a short briefing paper on the Incident Management Team (IMT) approach to dealing with long-term campaign incidents (see page 124). Include point of contact information for your state IMT, if one exists.
5. Go to http://www.8stepprocess.com for additional information and activities pertaining to Chapter 3 "Managing the Incident: Incident Command System."

STUDY GROUP ACTIVITY

1. One member of your group should *briefly* describe an incident from his or her own personal experience in which ICS was not implemented at an incident, to the detriment of the outcome. Then as a group, everyone should propose ways in which the identified problems could have been minimized or avoided by a properly implemented ICS.

2. In this exercise you will examine the pros and cons of "people-dependent" and "system-dependent" response programs. Divide into two groups. One group will develop the pros and cons of "people-dependent" programs, while the other group develops the pros and cons of "system-dependent" programs. The groups should rejoin and discuss their findings.
3. As a group, consider and discuss your reactions to the statement on page 98 in the textbook: "In those cases where ICS has not resulted in the operational improvements expected, the problems are typically associated with planning, training, and the organization buying into the ICS program, as compared to the ICS system itself." Each member of the group should provide examples to support or refute this statement.
4. As a group, consider and discuss your reactions to the statement on page 120: "There are no experts but only information sources." Each member of the group should provide examples to support or refute this statement.

STUDY GROUP LEARNING THROUGH INQUIRY SCENARIO 3-1

You are the Emergency Response Supervisor within a petrochemical manufacturing facility (e.g., chemical plant, refinery, petrochemical plant). A series of incidents prompted the Corporate Safety Office to commission a third party safety audit of your facility. The following issues have been identified by the audit team:

- Confidential interviews with managers, supervisors and operators have revealed strong evidence that the chain-of-command during an emergency is unclear.
- Interviews with Emergency Response Team members revealed that numerous supervisors and managers who have no emergency response training have been consistently reporting to the emergency scene. In many cases, these individuals do not wear appropriate levels of personal protective clothing.
- All emergency communications are maintained on a single emergency radio channel. This has led to numerous communications problems.
- The plant Emergency Operations Center (EOC) is maintained within the process area in a control room.
- Individuals are unclear as to their roles and responsibilities.

Your Plant Manager has asked you to give a presentation to the facility Management Team with your recommendations on how to resolve the problems identified by the audit. Based on the information provided, answer the following questions:

1) The Vice President of the company plans to attend the meeting. As a safety professional, you see this as a golden opportunity to implement much needed changes to your emergency response program. You have been given 30 minutes on the meeting agenda to give your presentation. What are the three main recommendations that you want to make? (Review the materials on Incident Command starting on page 92, Chapter 3.)
2) How will you handle your presentation to the Management Team knowing that many of the managers who will be present at the meeting are the same people that routinely report to the emergency scene without the proper training or equipment? You know they are part of the problem. (Review ICS Lessons Learned starting on page 96, Chapter 3.)

STUDY GROUP LEARNING THROUGH INQUIRY SCENARIO 3-3

You are the supervisor of a newly formed Hazardous Materials Response Team which is assigned to the Special Operations Division of the Fire Department. Your department has over 800 employees assigned to 22 stations. Your department uses the Incident Command System very effectively and appoints a Safety Officer on all working incidents. The new HMRT has been integrated smoothly into the command structure; however, you have had some significant problems distinguishing the difference between the incident Safety Officer and the HMRT Safety Officer. You are concerned about establishing the credibility of the HMRT within the command structure of the department.

You raise the issue at an Operations Division staff meeting and the Operations Chief asks you, "Why do we need two safety officers at the same incident?" Based on the information in Chapter 3 answer the following questions:

1) Are two Safety Officers really necessary at hazardous materials incidents? If you feel that the HMRT should have its own Safety Officer, how would you answer the Chief's question and justify your position? (Review Figure 3-5 on page 103, Chapter 3.)
2) From a functional perspective, what duties and responsibilities should the incident Safety Officer perform as compared to the HMRT Safety Officer?
3) From a political perspective, what can you do within the HMRT to assure that the system runs better?

SUMMARY AND REVIEW

1. ICS is predicated on basic management concepts, including the following division of labor and clearly defined lines of authority. Identify at least one other management concept:

2. Which of the following is the ICS organizational level that has functional responsibility for primary functions of emergency incident operation:
   a. Sections
   b. Branches
   c. Divisions/Groups/Sectors
   d. Command Staff

3. The ICS organizational structure develops in a ________ fashion based on the size and nature of the incident:
   a. Modular
   b. Linear
   c. Hierarchal
   d. Pyramid

4. When the ICP and the EOC are both operating simultaneously at a major incident, the ICP is primarily oriented towards tactical control issues pertaining to the on-scene response, while the EOC deals with:

5. List at least four equipment items that should be located at the EOC:

6. True / False: Communications of a sensitive nature should not be given over nonsecure cellular telephones or radios that can be monitored.

7. True / False: Unified command is not management by committee; there will always be a lead agency or one agency that has 51% of the vote as compared to the other players.

8. What is the most effective way to ensure that a consolidated plan of action is implemented:

Column A (below) lists the five primary functions and two secondary support functions assigned to the Hazardous Materials Group. Match each function to its respective tasks/responsibilities in Column B:

Column A Hazardous Materials Group Function	**Column B Tasks/Responsibilities**
9.________Safety function	A. Establishes hazard control zones, establishes and monitor egress routes at the incident site, and ensures that contaminants are not being spread.
10.________Entry/back-up function	B. Responsible for pre- and post-entry medical monitoring and evaluation of all entry personnel, and provides technical medical guidance to the Hazardous Materials Group, as requested.
11.________Decontamination function	C. Responsible for all entry and backup operations within the hot zone, including reconnaissance, monitoring, sampling, and mitigation.
12.________Site access control function	D. Responsible for ensuring that safe and accepted practices and procedures are followed throughout the course of the incident.

13._______Information/research function	E. Responsible for control and tracking of all supplies and equipment used by the Hazardous Materials Group during the course of an emergency.
14.______Medical function	F. Responsible for gathering, compiling, coordinating and disseminating all data and information relative to the incident.
15._______Resource function	G. Responsible for the research and development of the decon plan, set-up, and operation of an effective decontamination area capable of handling all potential exposures, including entry personnel, contaminated patients, and equipment.

16. The Hazardous Materials Group Supervisor will usually report to either the Incident Commander (IC) or the:
    a. Operations Section Chief
    b. HMRT Team Leader
    c. Safety Officer
    d. Hazardous Materials Branch Director

17. Which of the following Hazardous Materials Group staff is responsible for directing rescue operations within the Hot Zone:
    a. Decontamination Team
    b. Entry Team
    c. Site Access Control
    d. Hazardous Materials Medical Unit

18. Which of the following Hazardous Materials Group staff is responsible for providing recommendations for the selection and use of protective clothing and equipment:
    a. Decontamination Team
    b. Hazardous Materials Medical Unit
    c. Hazardous Materials Group Safety Officer
    d. Hazardous Materials Information/Research Team

19. In the heat of battle, the Operations Section may start to reduce the flow of information to the remainder of the ICS organization. Identify at least one way to avoid this problem:

20. In what ways can the Liaison Officer help manage the political issues of a hazmat incident:

SUMMARY AND REVIEW ANSWER KEY

1. To be correct, your answer must include at least one of the following:

   - Unity of command
   - Optimum span of control
   - Establishment of both line and staff functions within the organization. (p. 99)

2. a. Sections (p. 100)

3. a. Modular (p. 102)

4. The EOC deals with both strategic and external world issues and coordinates all logistical and resource support for on-scene operations. (p. 104)

5. To be correct, your answer should include at least four of the following:
   - Radio, phone, and fax communications
   - Area and facility maps, site plot plans, emergency preplans, hazard analysis documentation, and other related information.
   - Emergency response guidebooks and other reference sources (i.e., the Emergency Response Plan, the LEPC Plan, MSDSs, etc.)
   - Writing boards, incident status and documentation boards, telefax and copying machines.
   - Electronic communication capabilities (i.e., computers and e-mail, the Internet and intranet, agency-specific Web sites, etc.)
   - Television sets and AM/FM radios
   - Backup emergency power capability (p. 105)

6. True (p. 106)

7. True (p. 106)

8. The most effective way to ensure that a consolidated plan of action is implemented is to have the senior representative of each major player at the incident present at the ICP and/or EOC at all times. (p. 108)

Column A Hazardous Materials Group Function	**Column B Tasks/Responsibilities**
9.___D___Safety function (p. 109)	A. Establishes hazard control zones, establishes and monitor egress routes at the incident site, and ensures that contaminants are not being spread.
10.___C___Entry/back-up function (p. 109)	B. Responsible for pre- and post-entry medical monitoring and evaluation of all entry personnel, and provides technical medical guidance to the Hazardous Materials Group, as requested.

11. ___G___ Decontamination function (p. 109)

12. ___A___ Site access control function (p. 109)

13. ___F___ Information/research function (p. 109)

14. ___B___ Medical function (p. 109)

15. ___E___ Resource function (p. 109)

C. Responsible for all entry and backup operations within the hot zone, including reconnaissance, monitoring, sampling, and mitigation.

D. Responsible for ensuring that safe and accepted practices and procedures are followed throughout the course of the incident.

E. Responsible for control and tracking of all supplies and equipment used by the Hazardous Materials Group during the course of an emergency,

F. Responsible for gathering, compiling, coordinating and disseminating all data and information relative to the incident.

G. Responsible for the research and development of the decon plan, set-up, and operation of an effective decontamination area capable of handling all potential exposures, including entry personnel, contaminated patients, and equipment.

16. a. Operations Section Chief (p. 111)

17. b. Entry Team (p. 112)

18. d. Hazardous Materials Information/Research Team (p. 113)

19. To be correct, your answer should include at least one of the following:

    - Assign a communications aide to the Operations Section Officer
    - Establish procedures that require that updates and status reports be provided at timely intervals (e.g., every 10 minutes). (p. 117)

20. The Liaison Officer is sometimes viewed as the "Political Officer" who serves as the point of contact for all assisting and cooperating external and governmental representatives who are not represented within the unified command structure. The Liaison Officer allows the IC and general staff to focus on problem resolution while ensuring that political sensitivities are still addressed. The Liaison Officer's ability to effectively coordinate, handle, and, if necessary, "stroke" these individual agencies and representatives will have a significant impact on how the incident will be perceived from both a political and external perspective. (p. 118)

SELF EVALUATION

Please review all your work in this lesson. Now that you have completed this lesson, please take about 15 minutes to note your stronger and weaker areas.

Overall I feel I did (very well / well / fair / not so well) on the acronyms and abbreviations exercise.

Overall I feel I did (very well / well / fair / not so well) on the self-test questions.

Overall I feel I did (very well / well / fair / not so well) on the summary and review questions.

When compared to the previous lessons, I think I performed (better / worse / equally well).

List two areas in Chapter 3 in which you feel you could improve your skill or knowledge level:

1.

2.

Consider the following self-evaluation questions as they pertain to Chapter 3:

Am I taking effective margin notes?

Am I dedicating enough quality time to my studies?

Is anything distracting my focus?

Was any part of Chapter 3 too advanced for me?

Did I find that I don't have enough background experience to sufficiently grasp certain subject areas?

For areas in which I did particularly well, was it because I'm particularly interested in that subject matter? How so?

Were some things easier to learn because I have prior experience in learning or working with the concepts or principles?

Did I find that certain portions of the textbook seem to be better organized and effective in explaining key points?

What other Students have had to say about Chapter 3 material:

"ICS is not something you can just read about and expect to perform flawlessly in on your first time out. It requires practice and experience to become proficient.

The Incident Command System is a necessity during an incident. I feel that all parties involved with the incident must be trained and understand how the system works, and who is accountable to whom. If the system is not understood and used, chaos could result. If chaos occurs during a hazmat incident, lives could be lost.

As a lieutenant in a volunteer department, it is important for me to be knowledgeable and proficient not only in participating in, but also being able to establish and maintain a command at an incident if necessary. Only through studying and practicing the system can I become proficient and confident in my skills and knowledge.

The political aspect of hazmat response is one area in which I do not deal with on an everyday basis. This section helped me become more knowledgeable about political vulnerability for my future career.

Some times I believe dealing with political issues is my only duty. I work in a governmental environment and have to keep up with the ever changing responsibilities and personalities involved. Being able to handle those type of situations are critical.

The politics that are involved with some situations are often hard to understand. Sometimes people may not understand exactly who is in charge and what the objective is. Sometimes it is easy to say what someone else should have done. It's like being the Monday morning quarterback."

Pat on the Back

Congratulations on working though Chapter 3 in the textbook and for completing the exercises in this lesson.

CHAPTER 4

THE EIGHT STEP PROCESS©: AN OVERVIEW

CHAPTER ORIENTATION

Open the text to page 130. Take about 10 minutes to skim the chapter. Pay attention to the boldface subject headings. Read the titles to all the figures and note how they fit into the subject headings. Please read the introduction and summary sections carefully. Keep in mind that this chapter is designed as a "bridge chapter" that provides an overview of the Eight Step Process©, which is a systematic way of approaching a hazmat incident. You will learn about each step in the process in much greater detail as you progress through chapters 5-12. When you have finished looking through Chapter 4, respond to the following items. Please use the textbook as you jot down your comments in the spaces provided below:

1. In general terms, how does the use of standardized procedures, such as the Eight Step Process© impact on safety?

2. Reflect on your current level of knowledge or background experience about the Eight Step Process© as covered in Chapter 4. Where have you read about, learned about, or applied this knowledge in the past?

3. What sections or parts of Chapter 4 strike you as looking especially interesting?

4. What particular subjects in this chapter are important for a person in your position to master?

5. What do you predict will be the hardest things for you to learn in this chapter?

LEARNING OBJECTIVES

Turn to page 130 and examine the chapter objectives. When you have finished, respond to the following question:

1. Which objectives in Chapter 4 do you feel you can achieve right now, with a reasonable level of confidence?

As you read the sections of the chapter that deal with the objectives you have identified above, make sure your ideas or knowledge base match those of the authors. If not, you should examine how your current understanding of the material differs from that of the authors'. Depending on the level at which you wish to master the subject, discrepancies will have to be rectified and gaps will need to be filled.

ABBREVIATIONS AND ACRONYMS

The following abbreviations and acronyms are used in Chapter 4:

APR	Air Purifying Respirator (p. 138)
DECON	Decontamination (p. 132, 133, 137, 140, 141, 142, 143, 144)
EOC	Emergency Operations Center (p. 139)
IAP	Incident Action Plan (p. 135, 136, 137)

IC	Incident Commander (p. 131)
ICP	Incident Command Post (p. 132, 138, 139)
IED	Improvised Explosive Devices (p. 135)
LPG	Liquefied Petroleum Gas (p. 132)
PASS	Personal Alert Safety System (p. 137)
PERO	Postemergency Response Operations (p. 143)
PPA	Public Protective Actions (p. 133)
PPE	Personal Protective Equipment (p. 137, 140, 142)
PPV	Positive Pressure Ventilation (p. 141)
SBCCOM	U.S. Army Soldiers Biological and Chemical Command (p. 142)
SWAT	Special Weapons and Tactics Team (p. 142)

Locate these abbreviations and acronyms in the textbook (page numbers provided above) and underline them. Read the paragraph in which they are used.

Word Search: Locate the abbreviations and acronyms for each of the following terms in the word puzzle below. Some letters will be used more than once.

For more challenge, solve this puzzle in your study group. The first person to find all the abbreviations and acronyms wins.

G D K K I Z U A X O P Q S S P
G K X C B K W E N R J D B O B
S Z P U Q I Z P A E E C T S P
W S F X C E U Q P P C A A V M
R I A M U Z T K W O W Q O Y O
Q G X P R S H J M S X H W W U
U J U F C O Y V L M O Z G E J
H S M U D E I A U E G C P F C
N O C E D K G P C T S P Q O X
Y H I S G P L P G V M D J E V
F V A W P N M O G W H W T Q Y
Y K P Z B N K D K P J J B P B
P P V R H S A P R E L S Z V E
H O M C U I M Q D U O X T T N
E A A N W C N F O X P C N K O

The Word Search Answer Key is at the end of this chapter.

STUDY SESSION OVERVIEW

Read pages 130 to 144. Take margin notes as you go. Underline or highlight phrases that you feel are important.

When you have completed your reading, respond to the following questions. You may use the textbook to help you answer the questions, or work from memory.

1. The eight functions in the Eight Step Process typically follow an implementation timeline at the incident. Based on your current understanding of the eight steps, which one is most likely to be ongoing throughout the entire incident until it is terminated?

2. Which of the Eight Step Process functions is considered the foundation on which all subsequent response functions and tactics are built?

3. Which comes first: conducting hazard and risk evaluation or selecting personal protective clothing and equipment?

4. Which comes first: committing personnel to the hot zone or evaluating the hazards and risks?

5. Which comes first: developing an incident action plan or evaluating the hazards and risks?

6. What would be your primary concerns when conducting mass decon operations at an incident involving possible terrorism? How would you address them?

7. In your own words, why is it important to formally terminate the incident?

SELF-TEST:

Answer the following questions. You may use the textbook to help you answer the questions, or work from memory.

Match each of the steps in the Eight Step Process© (Column A) to its respective goal in Column B:

Column A 8-STEP PROCESS	Column B GOAL
1.______Site Management and Control	A. To ensure that all emergency response personnel have the appropriate level of personal protective clothing and equipment for the expected tasks.
2.______Identify the Problem	B. To ensure that the incident priorities (i.e., rescue, incident stabilization, environmental and property protection) are accomplished in a safe, timely, and effective manner.
3.______Hazard and Risk Evaluation	C. To ensure the safety of both emergency responders and the public by reducing the level of contamination on scene and minimizing the potential for secondary contamination beyond the incident scene.
4.______Select Personal Protective Clothing and Equipment	D. To establish the playing field so that all subsequent response operations can be implemented both safety and effectively.
5.______Information Management and Resource Coordination	E. To identify the scope and nature of the problem, including the type and nature of hazardous materials involved as appropriate.
6.______Implement Response Objectives	F. To provide for the timely and effective management, coordination, and dissemination of all pertinent data, information, and resources between all of the players.
7.______Decon and Clean-Up Operations	G. To ensure that overall command is transferred to the proper agency when the emergency is terminated and that all post-incident administrative activities are completed per local policies and procedures.

8.______Terminate the Incident

H. To assess the hazards present, evaluate the level of risk, and establish an Incident Action Plan (IAP) to make the problem go away.

9. Which of the following functions establishes the playing field for the Players (responders) and the Spectators (everyone else):
[p. 133]
a. Site Management and Control
b. Hazard and Risk Evaluation
c. Information Management and Resource Coordination
d. Implement Response Objectives

10. Site Management and Control involves:
[p. 133]
a. Establishing a hot zone
b. Analyzing container shapes
c. Consulting technical information specialists
d. Selecting personal protective clothing

11. The primary objective of the risk evaluation process is to:
[p. 135]
a. Identify the presence of improvised explosive devices (IED)
b. Verify the hazardous materials involved in the incident
c. Determine whether or not responders should intervene
d. Initiate public protective actions

12. Which of the following functions cannot be effectively accomplished unless a unified ICS organization is in place:
[p. 138]
a. Site Management and Control
b. Hazard and Risk Evaluation
c. Select Personal Protective Clothing and Equipment
d. Information Management and Resource Coordination

13. Which of the following strategies is not a defensive mode response objective:
[p. 140]
a. Rescue
b. Fire control
c. Spill control
d. Public protective actions

14. The termination of emergency response operations includes which of the following activities:
[p. 143]
a. Decontamination
b. Clean-up operations
c. Leak control
d. Incident debriefing

ANSWER KEY

Check your answers. If you missed more than three, you should read the chapter once again.

Column A 8-STEP PROCESS	Column B GOAL
1. __D__ Site Management and Control (p. 132)	A. To ensure that all emergency response personnel have the appropriate level of personal protective clothing and equipment for the expected tasks.
2. __E__ Identify the Problem (p. 134)	B. To ensure that the incident priorities (i.e., rescue, incident stabilization, environmental and property protection) are accomplished in a safe, timely, and effective manner.
3. __H__ Hazard and Risk Evaluation (p. 135)	C. To ensure the safety of both emergency responders and the public by reducing the level of contamination on scene and minimizing the potential for secondary contamination beyond the incident scene.
4. __A__ Select Personal Protective Clothing and Equipment (p. 137)	D. To establish the playing field so that all subsequent response operations can be implemented both safety and effectively.
5. __F__ Information Management and Resource Coordination (p. 138)	E. To identify the scope and nature of the problem, including the type and nature of hazardous materials involved as appropriate.
6. __B__ Implement Response Objectives (p. 140)	F. To provide for the timely and effective management, coordination, and dissemination of all pertinent data, information, and resources between all of the players.
7. __C__ Decon and Clean-Up Operations (p. 141)	G. To ensure that overall command is transferred to the proper agency when the emergency is terminated and that all post-incident administrative activities are completed per local policies and procedures.
8. __G__ Terminate the Incident (p. 143)	H. To assess the hazards present, evaluate the level of risk, and establish an Incident Action Plan (IAP) to make the problem go away.

9. Which of the following functions establishes the playing field for the Players (responders) and the Spectators (everyone else):
   [p. 133]
   a. Site Management and Control
   b. Hazard and Risk Evaluation
   c. Information Management and Resource Coordination
   d. Implement Response Objectives

10. Site Management and Control involves:
[p. 133]
a. Establishing a hot zone
b. Analyzing container shapes
c. Consulting technical information specialists
d. Selecting personal protective clothing

11. The primary objective of the risk evaluation process is to:
[p. 135]
a. Identify the presence of improvised explosive devices (IED)
b. Verify the hazardous materials involved in the incident
c. Determine whether or not responders should intervene
d. Initiate public protective actions

12. Which of the following functions cannot be effectively accomplished unless a unified ICS organization is in place:
[p. 138]
a. Site Management and Control
b. Hazard and Risk Evaluation
c. Select Personal Protective Clothing and Equipment
d. Information Management and Resource Coordination

13. Which of the following strategies is not a defensive mode response objective:
[p. 140]
a. Rescue
b. Fire control
c. Spill control
d. Public protective actions

14. The termination of emergency response operations includes which of the following activities:
[p. 143]
a. Decontamination
b. Clean-up operations
c. Leak control
d. Incident debriefing

PRACTICE

Assume you are responding to a train wreck within a half-mile of a mixed residential and business neighborhood in your community. There are 14 derailed cars, two of which are carrying 90 tons of chlorine each. One of the tank cars has ruptured and is releasing chlorine gas to the atmosphere. Match each of the emergency procedures listed in Column B to one of the Eight Steps in Column A. One answer is already provided (See Step 3). There are two procedures that match each step:

Column A

8-STEP PROCESS

Step 1: Site Management and Control

_____

_____

Step 2: Identify the Problem

_____

_____

Step 3: Hazard and Risk Evaluation

C

_____

Step 4: Select Personal Protective Clothing and Equipment

_____

_____

Step 5: Information Management and Resource Coordination

_____

_____

Step 6: Implement Response Objectives

_____

_____

Step 7: Decon and Clean-up Operations

_____

_____

Step 8: Terminate the Incident

_____

_____

Column B

PROCEDURE

A. Ensure proper decontamination of emergency personnel before they leave the scene.

B. Assure that site emergency workers are using the proper protective equipment and clothing equal to the hazards present.

C. Evaluate the risks of personnel intervening directly in the emergency.

D. Initiate offensive tactics which will reduce or stop the flow of chlorine if it can be accomplished without undue risk.

E. Confirm that your Command Post is in a safe area and that your position will not be overrun by the migrating vapor cloud.

F. Determine the concentrations of toxic gases present using both fixed monitors (if available) and portable instruments. What is the concentration of chlorine?

G. Identify, confirm, and verify the problem. If multiple problems exist, prioritize them and make independent assignments

H. Use a massive rinse on the outer shell of protective clothing. Maintain respiratory protection throughout the decontamination process.

I. Obtain the names and telephone numbers of all key individuals. Include contractors, public officials and members of the media.

J. Restrict access to the emergency site to authorized essential personnel

K. Determine the nature, extent and potential impact of the release

L. Establish a Command Post well outside the chlorine vapor cloud area

M. Order specialized equipment and expertise early in the incident. If you are unsure what your requirements are, always call for the highest level of assistance available.

N. Ensure that a properly equipped back-up rescue team is in-place before initiating offensive tactics.

O. Document all equipment or supplies used during the incident.

P. Coordinate your emergency plans with all support personnel. Make sure that they are aware of where the Hot, Warm, and Cold Zones are located and that special hazards are involved.

The answer key is at the end of this chapter.

Go to http://www.8stepprocess.com for additional information and activities pertaining to Chapter 4 "The Eight Step Process: An Overview."

STUDY GROUP ACTIVITY

1. As a group, review and discuss the street smart tips for each of the eight-step process functions. Identify those that you feel are particularly important or valid.
2. Brainstorm ways in which security issues can be handled or anticipated using the principles of the eight-step process. Be sure to consider all eight steps, in sequence.

STUDY GROUP LEARNING THOUGH INQUIRY SCENARIO 4-1

You are a Battalion Fire Chief assigned to lead a Post-Incident Analysis Team investigating a firefighter fatality. The Fire Chief wants to know if the department's standard operating procedures were followed.

The incident involved a warehouse that stored 18,000 one pound LPG cylinders in an unsprinklered building. When the first engine company arrived at 3:00 am the fire was venting through the skylight in the center of the warehouse. The company officer ordered an interior fire attack using handlines. When the Battalion Fire Chief arrived on scene the propane cylinders began to fail, intensifying the fire. The engine company was ordered out of the building, but a partial roof collapse trapped one firefighter.

1) Using the 8 Step Process shown on page 132, Chapter 4, determine what step in the process was the first arriving engine company engaged in when the Battalion Chief ordered the company from inside the warehouse?

2) What step in the 8 Step Process was the Battalion Fire Chief assigned to during the Post Incident Analysis?

3) During your interview with the Battalion Fire Chief who commanded the fire, he informs you that he believed that the engine company officer failed to consider the risk of the propane cylinders inside the warehouse and this was the major contributing fac-

tor in the firefighter fatality. Do you agree with this statement? If so, why? If you disagree, what is the basis for this opinion? (Review the material on pages 135 to 137 and use this to support your opinion.)

SUMMARY AND REVIEW

1. There are eight basic functions that must be evaluated at emergencies involving, or suspected on involving hazmats or WMD agents. Several of these functions are provided below. Fill in the blanks with the remaining functions, in correct sequence:

   Step 1. Site Management and Control

   Step 2. ______________________________

   Step 3. ______________________________

   Step 4. Select Personal Protective Clothing and Equipment

   Step 5. ______________________________

   Step 6. Implement Response Objectives

   Step 7. ______________________________

   Step 8. Terminate the Incident

2. Which of the Eight Step Process functions is concerned with carrying our a smooth and safe transition from the emergency phase of the incident to the clean-up and recovery Phase?

3. Which of the Eight Step Process functions is concerned with conducting an incident debriefing session for on-scene response personnel?

4. Which of the Eight Step Process functions is concerned with providing regular updates to the local Emergency Operations Center (EOC), if activated?

5. What is the minimum level of training at which personnel should be able to deliver an emergency decon:
   a. First Responder —Awareness
   b. First Responder —Operations
   c. Hazardous Materials Technician
   d. EMS/HM Level I

6. Why does the selection of personal protective clothing and equipment come after Hazard and Risk Evaluation instead of ahead of Hazard and Risk Evaluation?

7. Identify at least three primary objectives of Step One: Site Management and Control:

8. You are the Incident Commander at a chemical plant fire. You have decided to implement non-intervention mode until additional personnel and equipment arrive. Identify one non-intervention tactic that should be initiated.

9. List three clues that an improvised explosive device (IED) may be present at an incident.

10. A security officer on patrol on the ground level of a hospital parking garage smells a strong odor of gas. The officer calls 911 and requests that the fire department respond. The fire department dispatches one engine company to investigate. You are the company officer on the response.
    a) What other information would you want to know while en-route?

    b) Identify three ways you could perform defensive recon:

    c) Identify two or three ways to perform offensive recon:

11. There are three critical success factors in hour 1 of a hazmat response. The first is the ability of the responders to recognize clues that the incident may involve hazardous materials. What are the other two factors?

SUMMARY AND REVIEW ANSWER KEY

1. Step 1. Site Management and Control
   Step 2. Identify the Problem
   Step 3. Hazard and Risk Evaluation
   Step 4. Select Personal Protective Clothing and Equipment
   Step 5. Information Management and Resource Coordination
   Step 6. Implement Response Objectives
   Step 7. Decon and Clean-up Operations
   Step 8. Terminate the Incident (p.132)

2. Step 8: Terminate the Incident (p. 143)

3. Step 8: Terminate the Incident (p. 143)

4. Step 5: Information Management and Resource Coordination (p. 138)

5. b. First Responder—Operations (p. 141)

6. Because the selection of personal protective clothing will depend not only on the hazards and properties of the materials involved, but also the response objectives to be implemented (i.e., offensive, defensive, or nonintervention.) Whether the incident should be handled offensively, defensively, or by nonintervention is determined in Step 3: Hazard and Risk Evaluation. (p. 136-137)

7. To be correct, your answer should include at least three of the following:
   - Establish Command
   - Establish a staging area
   - Establish and control an isolation perimeter
   - Establish hazard control zones (hot zone, warm zone, cold zone)
   - Initiate public protective actions (i.e., evacuate the threatened population and/or protect them in place)

   (p.132-133)

8. Public protective actions (p. 136)

9. To be correct, your answer should include any three of the following:
   - Abandoned container out of place for the surroundings
   - Obvious explosive device components, such as batteries, timers, blasting caps, charges
   - Partially exploded devices found
   - Unusual or foreign devices attached to hazmat containers, especially liquefied and compressed gas cylinders, flammable liquid containers and bulk storage tanks and vessels
   - Unattended vehicles not appropriate to the immediate environment (p. 135)

10. a) What other information would you want to know while en-route?
   - Where is the location of the incident? Is the incident at a target occupancy or target hazard event? Is there a preincident plan for the location?
   - Are hazmats involved? If unsure, are hazmats found at the location?
   - Are there reports of any unusual odors? Explosions? Hazardous materials?
   - Are any injuries or casualties involved? Are the reasons known or unknown? (p. 131)

   b) Identify three ways you could perform defensive recon:
   - Threat assessments, interviews, physical observations, etc. (p. 134)

   c) Identify two or three ways to perform offensive recon:
   - Conduct monitoring, sampling, or video/photo documentation for analysis. (p. 134)

11.
   - The ability of responders to quickly gain control of the incident scene and separate responders and others from the problem
   - The ability to establish command and control in a timely manner (p. 131)

Word Search Answer Key:

G	D	K	K	I	Z	U	A	X	O	P	Q	S	S	P
G	K	X	C	B	K	W	E	N	R	J	D	B	O	B
S	Z	P	U	Q	I	Z	P	A	E	E	C	T	S	P
W	S	F	X	C	E	U	Q	P	P	C	A	A	V	M
R	I	A	M	U	Z	T	K	W	O	W	Q	O	Y	O
Q	G	X	P	R	S	H	J	M	S	X	H	W	W	U
U	J	U	F	C	O	Y	V	L	M	O	Z	G	E	J
H	S	M	U	D	E	I	A	U	E	G	C	P	F	C
N	O	C	E	D	K	G	P	C	T	S	P	Q	O	X
Y	H	I	S	G	P	L	P	G	V	M	D	J	E	V
F	V	A	W	P	N	M	O	G	W	H	W	T	Q	Y
Y	K	P	Z	B	N	K	D	K	P	J	J	B	P	B
P	P	V	R	H	S	A	P	R	E	L	S	Z	V	E
H	O	M	C	U	I	M	Q	D	U	O	X	T	T	N
E	A	A	N	W	C	N	F	O	X	P	C	N	K	O

Practice Exercise Answer Key:

Step 1: Site Management and Control

J) Restrict access to the emergency site to authorized essential personnel

L) Establish a Command Post well outside the chlorine vapor cloud area

Step 2: Identify the Problem

G) Identify, confirm, and verify the problem. If multiple problems exist, prioritize them and make independent assignments

K) Determine the nature, extent and potential impact of the release.

Step 3: Hazard and Risk Evaluation

C) Evaluate the risks of personnel intervening directly in the emergency.

F) Determine the concentrations of toxic gases present using both fixed monitors (if available) and portable instruments. What is the concentration of chlorine?

Step 4: Select Personal Protective Clothing and Equipment

B) Assure that site emergency workers are using the proper protective equipment and clothing equal to the hazards present.

M) Order specialized equipment and expertise early in the incident. If you are unsure what your requirements are, always call for the highest level of assistance available.

Step 5: Information Management and Resource Coordination

E) Confirm that your Command Post is in a safe area and that your position will not be overrun by the migrating vapor cloud.

P) Coordinate your emergency plans with all support personnel. Make sure that they are aware of where the Hot, Warm, and Cold Zones are located and that special hazards are involved.

Step 6: Implement Response Objectives

D) Initiate offensive tactics which will reduce or stop the flow of chlorine if it can be accomplished without undue risk.

N) Ensure that a properly equipped back-up rescue team is in-place before initiating offensive tactics.

Step 7: Decon and Clean-up Operations

A) Ensure proper decontamination of emergency personnel before they leave the scene.

H) Use a massive rinse on the outer shell of protective clothing. Maintain respiratory protection throughout the decontamination process.

Step 8: Terminate the Incident

I) Obtain the names and telephone numbers of all key individuals. Include contractors, public officials and members of the media.

O) Document all equipment or supplies used during the incident.

SELF EVALUATION

Please review all your work in this lesson. Now that you have completed this lesson, please take about 15 minutes to note your stronger and weaker areas.

Overall I feel I did (very well / well / fair / not so well) on the acronyms and abbreviations exercise.

Overall I feel I did (very well / well / fair / not so well) on the self-test questions.

Overall I feel did (very well / well / fair / not so well) on the practice exercise.

Overall I feel I did (very well / well / fair / not so well) on the summary and review questions.

When compared to the previous lessons, I think I performed (better / worse / equally well).

List two areas in Chapter 4 in which you feel you could improve your skill or knowledge level:

1.

2.

Consider the following self-evaluation questions as they pertain to Chapter 4:

Am I taking effective margin notes?

Am I dedicating enough quality time to my studies?

Is anything distracting my focus?

Was any part of Chapter 4 too advanced for me?

Did I find that I don't have enough background experience to sufficiently grasp certain subject areas?

For areas in which I did particularly well, was it because I'm particularly interested in that subject matter? How so?

Were some things easier to learn because I have prior experience in learning or working with the concepts or principles?

Did I find that certain portions of the textbook seem to be better organized and effective in explaining key points?

What other Students have had to say about Chapter 4 material:

> "The tactical part of a hazmat incident is one of my stronger points. I feel that I understand the Eight Step Process really well."
>
> "I carry a command note book with me while I am on duty. The command notebook it has "cheat sheets," IMS forms, and contact numbers. One of my cheat sheets is a photocopy of the Eight Step Process as taken from the Fire Chiefs Handbook 5th ed. The Eight Step Process is a great tool for managing a hazmat incident."
>
> "The Eight Step process is firefighter friendly, and essentially firefighter proof. My team members have a lock on the Eight Step Process. In fact, when I interview for the technical rescue team the Eight Step Process is one of the areas I explore."
>
> "The Eight Step Process is tattooed on my firefighter psyche."

Pat on the Back

Congratulations on working though Chapter 4 in the textbook and for completing the exercises in this lesson.

CHAPTER 5
SITE MANAGEMENT

CHAPTER ORIENTATION

Open the text to page 149. Take about 10 minutes to skim the chapter. Pay attention to the boldface subject headings. Read the titles to all the figures and note how they fit into the subject headings. Scan the case studies. Please read the introduction and summary sections carefully. When you have finished looking through Chapter 5, respond to the following items. Please use the textbook as you jot down your comments in the spaces provided below:

1. In general terms, what makes learning how to establish control of the incident scene so important?

2. Reflect on your current level of knowledge or background experience about site management and control. Where have you read about, learned about, or applied the principles of site management and control in the past?

3. What sections or parts of Chapter 5 strike you as looking especially interesting?

4. What particular aspects of site management and control are important for a person in your position to master?

5. What do you predict will be the hardest things for you to learn in this chapter?

LEARNING OBJECTIVES

Turn to page 150 and examine the chapter objectives. When you have finished, respond to the following question:

1. Which objectives in Chapter 5 do you feel you can achieve right now, with a reasonable level of confidence?

Highlight or place a check mark next to those objectives on page 150 that addresses educational competencies referenced in *NFPA 472—Professional Competence of Responders to Hazardous Materials.*

As you read the sections of the chapter that deal with the objectives you have identified above, make sure your ideas or knowledge base match those of the authors. If not, you should examine how your current understanding of the material differs from that of the authors'. Depending on the level at which you wish to master the subject, discrepancies will have to be rectified and gaps will need to be filled.

ABBREVIATIONS AND ACRONYMS

The following abbreviations and acronyms are used in Chapter 5:

CPC	Chemical Protective Clothing (p. 160)
EAS	Emergency Alerting System (p. 182)
EBA	Escape Breathing Apparatus (p. 185)
ICP	Incident Command Post (p. 153, 155, 157, 159, 162, 186)
IDLH	Immediately Dangerous to Life and Health (p. 158, 166)
MOU	Memorandum of Understanding (p. 180, 185)
PPA	Public Protective Action (p. 161, 165, 174)
SBS	Sick Building Syndrome (p. 173, 174)
VOC	Volatile Organic Compounds (p. 173)

Locate these abbreviations and acronyms in the textbook (page numbers provided above) and underline them. Read the paragraph in which they are used.

For each of the following sentences, write in the correct abbreviation or acronym (from the list above) so that that sentence makes sense:

1. Research shows that some ___________ can cause chronic and acute health effects at high concentrations.

2. While specific causes of _______ remain unknown, chemical contaminants from outdoor sources may be a contributing factor.

3. The vendor offered three models of ________ in five and ten minute units.

4. The safety officer had trouble locating any federal standards that directly required a minimum of two standby persons at _______ incidents.

5. Some of the personnel were ordered to report directly to the _______ to assist the Incident Commander.

6. Television and radio are excellent methods with which to coordinate and manage large-scale ______________ activities.

7. When used in conjunction with air supplied respiratory protection devices, _________ offers a sealed, integral level of full-body protection from a hostile environment.

8. An ______ should be in place between the fire department and the agency providing food services.

9. According to the manual, ______ is an effective method of alerting people in buildings and automobiles.

ANSWER KEY

1. Research shows that some VOC can cause chronic and acute health effects at high concentrations.

2. While specific causes of SBS remain unknown, chemical contaminants from outdoor sources may be a contributing factor.

3. The vendor offered three models of EBA in five and ten minute units.

4. The safety officer had trouble locating any federal standards that directly required a minimum of two standby persons at IDLH incidents.

5. Some of the personnel were ordered to report directly to the ICP to assist the Incident Commander.

6. Television and radio are excellent methods with which to coordinate and manage large-scale PPA activities.

7. When used in conjunction with air supplied respiratory protection devices, CPC offers a sealed, integral level of full-body protection from a hostile environment.

8. An MOU should be in place between the fire department and the agency providing food services.

9. According to the manual, EAS is an effective method of alerting people in buildings and automobiles.

STUDY SESSION OVERVIEW

Read pages 151 to 160, then take a short break to think about what you have read. Then read the rest of the chapter. Take margin notes as you go. Underline or highlight phrases that you feel are important.

When you have completed your reading, respond to the following questions. You may use the textbook to help you answer the questions, or work from memory.

1. In your own words, what safety issues are associated with site management and control?

2. What can happen at a hazmat incident if there is no strong, centralized command?

3. In what ways do the lessons learned from the Houston (TX) anhydrous ammonia/freeway incident (page 166) help advance our tactical understanding of site management and control?

4. How did good site management and control influence the outcome of the CSX tunnel fire in Baltimore, Maryland? (p. 178-179).

SELF-TEST:

Answer the following questions. You may use the textbook to help you answer the questions, or work from memory.

1. The major emphasis of Site Management is on establishing control of the incident scene and: [p. 151]
   a. Gathering information
   b. Designating safety zones
   c. Isolating people from the problem
   d. Alerting the public

2. The isolation perimeter is always the line between the: [p. 151]
   a. The inner perimeter and the outer perimeter
   b. General public and the cold zone
   c. Area of refuge and the hot zone
   d. Immediate site of the spill and staging area

3. Level 2 staging is usually reserved for: [p. 154]
   a. Large, complex, or lengthy hazmat operations
   b. Transportation-related hazmat incidents
   c. Incidents requiring decontamination
   d. Incidents requiring full-scale evacuation

4. Site management consists of all of the following tasks, except one: [p. 152]
   a. Assuming command
   b. Establishing staging
   c. Implementing initial public protective actions
   d. Implementing defensive confinement tactics

5. Staging procedures facilitate safety and: [p. 154]
   a. Command presence
   b. Back-up refuge
   c. Accountability
   d. Perimeter security

6. The following statements about the isolation perimeter are all true, except one:
[p. 155]
   a. The isolation perimeter is set up to maintain safety and security
   b. Designating the isolation perimeter is an Incident Command responsibility
   c. Proper protective clothing and equipment must be worn when establishing the isolation perimeter
   d. Isolation perimeters are not practical for indoor hazmat incidents

7. The primary purpose of establishing three different hazard control zones is to:
[p. 156]
   a. Assist initial size-up
   b. Allocate resources more efficiently
   c. Provide control and personnel accountability
   d. Reduce radio communications

8. The area of refuge should be established within the:
[p. 157]
   a. Hot zone
   b. Warm zone
   c. Cold zone
   d. Staging area

9. Decisions regarding the size of hazard control zones should be based on measures of:
[p. 158]
   a. Flammability
   b. Toxicity
   c. Radioactivity
   d. All of the above

10. The following points all apply to hazard control zones, except one:
[p. 159]
   a. Hazard Control Zones should be marked and posted on the IC's tactical command worksheet
   b. Initial monitoring efforts should concentrate on determining if IDLH concentrations are present.
   c. Once established, hazard control zones should not change or be modified
   d. Property owners should be briefed on how and why you have established hazard control zones

11. Public protective actions (PPAs) are the strategy used by the Incident Commander to protect the general public from the hazmat by implementing:
[p. 161]
   a. Protection-in-place
   b. Evacuation
   c. Either Protection-in-place *or* evacuation, but never both at the same time
   d. Either Protection-in-place, evacuation, or a combination of both

12. Protection-in-place is usually the best option when any of the following conditions exist, except one:
[p. 164]

a. Explosive or reactive materials are involved
b. Leaks can be rapidly controlled at their source
c. Short-duration solid or liquid leaks are present
d. The hazmat has been totally released from its container and is dissipating

13. The rating system for evaluating structures for protection-in-place is based primarily on criteria concerning:
[p. 169]
a. The "tightness" and age of the structure
b. The size of the structure
c. The occupancy of the structure
d. Terrain surrounding the structure

14. The following are all indicators of sick buildings, except one:
[p. 173]
a. Building occupants complain of symptoms associated with acute discomfort, such as headache
b. Building occupants complain of fatigue and/or difficulty in concentrating
c. The symptoms are caused by a known hazmat spill inside the building
d. Most complainants report relief soon after leaving the building

15. A study conducted by the Battelle Human Affairs Research Center indicated that the cost to the manufacturing sector for full-scale evacuation is approximately ____ the cost of protection-on-place:
[p. 175]
a. Twice
b. Three times
c. Seven times
d. Fifteen times

16. When the decision is made to commit to a full-scale public evacuation, four critical issues must be addressed and managed effectively – 1) alerting and notification; 2) transportation; 3) relocation facility; and 4):
[p. 177]
a. Monitoring
b. Information
c. Manpower
d. Multi-agency coordination

17. One of the most frequent alerting system problems encountered in fixed facilities (such as a refinery) is:
[p. 183]
a. Not knowing where to go once the alarm sounds
b. Hesitancy among workers to leave workstations unattended
c. Accounting for the whereabouts of contractors and visitors
d. The confusion created by a single warning tone that may also be used to indicate the beginning or ending of a work shift

18. A good community alerting and notification system is based on: [p. 183]
   a. Low-power AM radio systems
   b. Sirens and alarms
   c. Door-to-door visits
   d. A variety of warning systems

ANSWER KEY

Check your answers. If you missed more than five, you should read the chapter once again.

1. The major emphasis of Site Management is on establishing control of the incident scene and: [p. 151]
   a. Gathering information
   b. Designating safety zones
   c. Isolating people from the problem
   d. Alerting the public

2. The isolation perimeter is always the line between the: [p. 151]
   a. The inner perimeter and the outer perimeter
   b. General public and the cold zone
   c. Area of refuge and the hot zone
   d. Immediate site of the spill and staging area

3. Level 2 staging is usually reserved for: [p. 154]
   a. Large, complex, or lengthy hazmat operations
   b. Transportation-related hazmat incidents
   c. Incidents requiring decontamination
   d. Incidents requiring full-scale evacuation

4. Site management consists of all of the following tasks, except one: [p. 152]
   a. Assuming command
   b. Establishing staging
   c. Implementing initial public protective actions
   d. Implementing defensive confinement tactics

5. Staging procedures facilitate safety and: [p. 154]
   a. Command presence
   b. Back-up refuge
   c. Accountability
   d. Perimeter security

6. The following statements about the isolation perimeter are all true, except one: [p. 155]
   a. The isolation perimeter is set up to maintain safety and security
   b. Designating the isolation perimeter is an Incident Command responsibility

c. Proper protective clothing and equipment must be worn when establishing the isolation perimeter
d. Isolation perimeters are not practical for indoor hazmat incidents

7. The primary purpose of establishing three different hazard control zones is to:
[p. 156]
a. Assist initial size-up
b. Allocate resources more efficiently
c. Provide control and personnel accountability
d. Reduce radio communications

8. The area of refuge should be established within the:
[p. 157]
a. Hot zone
b. Warm zone
c. Cold zone
d. Staging area

9. Decisions regarding the size of hazard control zones should be based on measures of:
[p. 158]
a. Flammability
b. Toxicity
c. Radioactivity
d. All of the above

10. The following points all apply to hazard control zones, except one:
[p. 159]
a. Hazard Control Zones should be marked and posted on the IC's tactical command worksheet
b. Initial monitoring efforts should concentrate on determining if IDLH concentrations are present.
c. Once established, hazard control zones should not change or be modified
d. Property owners should be briefed on how and why you have established hazard control zones

11. Public protective actions (PPAs) are the strategy used by the Incident Commander to protect the general public from the hazmat by implementing:
[p. 161]
a. Protection-in-place
b. Evacuation
c. Either Protection-in-place *or* evacuation, but never both at the same time
d. Either Protection-in-place, evacuation, or a combination of both

12. Protection-in-place is usually the best option when any of the following conditions exist, except one:
[p. 164]
a. Explosive or reactive materials are involved
b. Leaks can be rapidly controlled at their source
c. Short-duration solid or liquid leaks are present
d. The hazmat has been totally released from its container and is dissipating

13. The rating system for evaluating structures for protection-in-place is based primarily on criteria concerning:
[p. 169]
   a. The "tightness" and age of the structure
   b. The size of the structure
   c. The occupancy of the structure
   d. Terrain surrounding the structure

14. The following are all indicators of sick buildings, except one:
[p. 173]
   a. Building occupants complain of symptoms associated with acute discomfort, such as headache
   b. Building occupants complain of fatigue and / or difficulty in concentrating
   c. The symptoms are caused by a known hazmat spill inside the building
   d. Most complainants report relief soon after leaving the building

15. A study conducted by the Battelle Human Affairs Research Center indicated that the cost to the manufacturing sector for full-scale evacuation is approximately ____ the cost of protection-on-place:
[p. 175]
   a. Twice
   b. Three times
   c. Seven times
   d. Fifteen times

16. When the decision is made to commit to a full-scale public evacuation, four critical issues must be addressed and managed effectively – 1) alerting and notification; 2) transportation; 3) relocation facility; and 4):
[p. 177]
   a. Monitoring
   b. Information
   c. Manpower
   d. Multi-agency coordination

17. One of the most frequent alerting system problems encountered in fixed facilities (such as a refinery) is:
[p. 183]
   a. Not knowing where to go once the alarm sounds
   b. Hesitancy among workers to leave workstations unattended
   c. Accounting for the whereabouts of contractors and visitors
   d. The confusion created by a single warning tone that may also be used to indicate the beginning or ending of a work shift

18. A good community alerting and notification system is based on:
[p. 183]
   a. Low-power AM radio systems
   b. Sirens and alarms
   c. Door-to-door visits
   d. A variety of warning systems

PRACTICE

1. Assume that a threat has been received that a car bomb is located in a parking garage nearby your state capitol. Using a large scale map and a sketch of the garage, diagram your initial isolation perimeter and explain your rationale. (Use separate sheets of paper for your practice exercise as needed.)

2. Develop a set of user-friendly instructions for your community that explains the concept of protection-in-place and provides clear instructions on what residents should do to shelter in their own homes. What advice would you give persons who live in Type III or Type IV structures? (see page 170 in the textbook.)

3. Assume that you have to alert visitors and staff at large regional park that a train carrying hazardous materials (unknown at this time) has derailed upwind of the park. Which of the alerting methods on pages 181-183 in the textbook would you use? Explain the basis for your selection. You should assume that the park includes trails, primitive camping, a lodge, several vendors, a large recreational lake, a dam, and two roads that lead to an interstate highway.

4. Look at Figure 5.19 on page 188 of the text. Then check your local telephone directory for similar emergency plan information. What suggestions can you offer that will make the information in your directory more useful or complete? For example, does it provide information on protection-in-place, evacuation routes, relocation facilities, Emergency Alert System radio stations, etc? If you directory does not contain any information, prepare an outline of key topics that should be included.

5. Go to http://www.8stepprocess.com for additional information and activities pertaining to Chapter 5 "Site Management."

IMPORTANT TERMINOLOGY

The following are all important terms that you should know. Go to page 151 and 152 and review the definitions:

Staging
Level I staging
Level II staging
Isolation perimeter
Hazard control zones
Hot zone
Warm zone
Cold zone
Area of refuge
Public protective actions (PPA)
Protection in-place
Evacuation

On the line next to each term in Column A, print the letter of its definition from Column B.

Column A Terminology	**Column B Definitions:**
1.______Staging	A. The designated crowd control line surrounding the Hazard Control Zones. The isolation perimeter is always the line between the general public and the Cold Zone. Law enforcement personnel may also refer to this as the outer perimeter.
2.______Level I staging	B. The control zone at a hazardous materials incident site where personnel and equipment decontamination and hot zone support takes place.
3.______Level II staging	C. The safe area established for temporary location of available resources closer to the incident site to reduce response time.
4.______Isolation perimeter	D. A holding area within the hot zone where personnel are controlled until they can be safely decontaminated or treated.
5.______Hazard control zones	E. The controlled relocation of people from an area of known danger or unacceptable risk to a safer area or one in which the risk is considered to be acceptable.
6.______Hot zone	F. The strategy used by the Incident Commander to protect the general population from the hazardous material by implementing a strategy of either (1) Protection-in-Place, (2) Evacuation, or (3) a combination of Protection-In-Place and Evacuation

7.______Warm zone

8.______Cold zone

9.______Area of refuge

10.______Public protective actions (PPA)

11.______Protection in-place

12.______Evacuation

G. The location where arriving units are initially sent when an incident escalates past the capability of the initial response. It is a tool usually reserved for large, complex, or lengthy hazmat operations.

H. The control zone immediately surrounding a hazardous materials incident that extends far enough to prevent adverse effects from hazardous materials releases to personnel outside the zone. Law enforcement personnel may also refer to this as the inner perimeter.

I. Directing people to go inside a building, seal it up as effectively as possible, and remain there until the danger from a hazardous materials release has passed.

J. The areas at a hazardous materials incident that contains the command post and other support functions necessary to control the incident.

K. Designation of areas at a hazardous materials incident based on safety and the degree of hazard. These zones are defined as the hot, warm, and cold zones.

L. The initial location for emergency response units at a multiple unit response to a hazmat incident. The first-arriving unit responds to the incident scene, while all other units are ordered to stage at a safe location close to, but away from the scene.

ANSWER KEY

Definitions are on p. 151-152

Column A
Terminology

1.__C__Staging

2.__L__Level I staging

3.__G__Level II staging

Column B
Definitions:

A. The designated crowd control line surrounding the Hazard Control Zones. The isolation perimeter is always the line between the general public and the Cold Zone. Law enforcement personnel may also refer to this as the outer perimeter.

B. The control zone at a hazardous materials incident site where personnel and equipment decontamination and hot zone support takes place.

C. The safe area established for temporary location of available resources closer to the incident site to reduce response time.

4.___A___Isolation perimeter

5.___K___Hazard control zones

6.___H___Hot zone

7.___B___Warm zone

8.___J___Cold zone

9.___D___Area of refuge

10.___F___Public protective actions (PPA)

11.___I___Protection in-place

12.___E___Evacuation

D. A holding area within the hot zone where personnel are controlled until they can be safely decontaminated or treated.

E. The controlled relocation of people from an area of known danger or unacceptable risk to a safer area or one in which the risk is considered to be acceptable.

F. The strategy used by the Incident Commander to protect the general population from the hazardous material by implementing a strategy of either (1) Protection-in-Place, (2) Evacuation, or (3) a combination of Protection-In-Place and Evacuation

G. The location where arriving units are initially sent when an incident escalates past the capability of the initial response. It is a tool usually reserved for large, complex, or lengthy hazmat operations.

H. The control zone immediately surrounding a hazardous materials incident that extends far enough to prevent adverse effects from hazardous materials releases to personnel outside the zone. Law enforcement personnel may also refer to this as the inner perimeter.

I. Directing people to go inside a building, seal it up as effectively as possible, and remain there until the danger from a hazardous materials release has passed.

J. The areas at a hazardous materials incident that contains the command post and other support functions necessary to control the incident.

K. Designation of areas at a hazardous materials incident based on safety and the degree of hazard. These zones are defined as the hot, warm, and cold zones.

L. The initial location for emergency response units at a multiple unit response to a hazmat incident. The first-arriving unit responds to the incident scene, while all other units are ordered to stage at a safe location close to, but away from the scene.

STUDY GROUP ACTIVITY

1. Working individually or in pairs, members of the group should conduct neighborhood surveys throughout their jurisdiction to identify the types of buildings present with regard to protection-in-place potential. Other group members should identify seasonal prevailing wind directions and topography that could affect the movement of toxic gas. Report your findings back to the group.

STUDY GROUP LEARNING THROUGH INQUIRY SCENARIO 5-1

You are a member of the Local Emergency Planning Committee (LEPC) within your community, and have been appointed chairperson of a subcommittee to review ideas for improving the system by which public protective actions are implemented as a result of a recent hazmat incident where some citizens had to be evacuated. Currently, the police department is responsible for implementing the evacuation order, school district buses are used for any transportation, and local schools and churches are used as evacuation centers. The agreements to provide these services have been long-standing but there is no formal arrangement. The community has no procedure for sheltering-in-place.

High hazard areas, which the LEPC has identified within the community, include two anhydrous ammonia storage facilities, a water treatment plant, several farm chemical facilities, an LPG and flammable liquid storage facility, a 4-lane state highway, and a major east/west railway corridor.

Based on the background information provided and the information provided on pages 180 –188 Chapter 5, respond to the following questions:

1) Based on what you know so far, are there any particular problems that you have identified which you feel should be addressed by your subcommittee? Develop a prioritized list of your top three concerns.
2) Based on the hazards identified in the community, which ones will place the community at greatest risk in terms of the need for public protective actions?
3) In your opinion, does this level of risk justify the time it would take to sell members of the LEPC on the concept of sheltering or protection-in-place? If you believe that it is worth the time, how would you develop and support your position to the LEPC?
4) Assuming that the LEPC supports your proposal on the concept of sheltering or protection-in-place, outline a plan-of-action for selling the concept to the community.

STUDY GROUP LEARNING THROUGH INQUIRY SCENARIO 5-2

You are the Fire Chief in a small town with a volunteer fire department. Under your leadership you have organized and conducted a series of emergency response exercises that were designed to test your community's ability to alert the public during a hazmat emergency. A major railway and highway pass through your community.

The most recent exercise revealed some significant findings. These include the following problems:

- The local 911 system cannot handle the influx of telephone calls that are expected during a major event such as a train derailment requiring evacuation. The local telephone company uses old equipment, but will not spend the money required to upgrade the system for an event that may never happen.
- Your town has one AM/FM radio station that is staffed as a "live radio station" during the day, but uses a taped unstaffed format from 8:00 PM to 5:00 AM. The recent test of the Emergency Broadcast System revealed that the EBS interrupt connection was not functioning properly. In other words, the EBS could not be activated.

Based on the background information provided and the information discussed in Chapter 5, respond to the following questions:

1) Based on the two problems identified during the exercise critique, how could you overcome these problems? Could you build an effective alerting and notification system? If you answered yes, what major elements would you build your Public Protective Action Plan on?

2) If you answered the question above no, how would you overcome these two significant problems?

3) If there were a real incident requiring an evacuation and several citizens were seriously injured, how would the image of your fire department be affected if the two problems described above were revealed in an investigation? What if you had previously identified these problems in an exercise but nothing was ever done about the problem. Would you be personally liable for failure to correct the problem? If you answered no, why wouldn't you be liable?

SUMMARY AND REVIEW

1. Define Site Management.

2. List the six major tasks that must be implemented as part of the site management and control process. Five are listed below. Which task is missing from this list?

   1) Assuming Command and establishing control of the incident scene
   2) Assuring safe approach and positioning of emergency response resources at the incident scene
   3) Establishing Staging as a method of controlling arriving resources
   4) Establishing Hazard Control Zones to assure a safe work area for emergency responders and supporting resources
   5) Sizing up the need for immediate rescue and implementing initial Public Protective Actions

3. There are two general guidelines for the safe approach and position of emergency response personal at a hazmat incident. One is to approach from uphill and upwind whenever possible. What is the other?

4. When is Level II Staging used?

5. Maintaining the isolation perimeter throughout the incident is usually the responsibility of:
   a. The staging officer
   b. Law enforcement or security professionals
   c. Initial arriving emergency response units
   d. Emergency preparedness personnel

6. What are the three public protective action strategies to protect the population from the hazardous material.

7. The IC's decision to evacuate or protect-in-place (or combination) should be based on several factors, including:

   - Hazardous material(s) involved, including their characteristics and properties, amount, concentrations, physical state, and location of release.
   - The population at risk, including facility personnel and the general public.
   - The time factors involved in the release.
   - The effects of the present and projected meteorological conditions on the control and movement of the hazardous materials release (temperature, precipitation, and wind conditions, etc).
   - The availability and capabilities of hazmat responders and other personnel to implement, control, monitor, and terminate the protective action.

   What is another factor?

8. The public is more likely to comply with instructions to protect-in-place when certain factors are present, including:
   - Receipt of a timely and an effective warning message.
   - Clear rationale for the decision to protect-in-place, as compared to an evacuation.
   - Credibility of emergency response personnel with the general public.

   What is another factor?

9. Two variables used in evaluating structures for protection-in-place are the age of the building and the prevailing wind direction (the direction the wind blows the majority of the time for the time of year in your area). What is another important variable?

10. A limited-scale evacuation may be the best option for the IC under the following conditions:

    - Whenever the building is on fire
    - Whenever the hazmat is leaking inside the building and the material is flammable or toxic
    - Whenever explosives or reactive materials are involved and can detonate or explode, producing flying glass or structural collapse
    - Whenever the building occupants show signs or symptoms of acute illness and there is a known hazmat spill inside the structure

What is another condition?

11. SBS is an abbreviation for:

12. The following are all situations that may justify a full-scale evacuation, except one:
    a. Large leaks involving flammable and/or toxic gases from large-capacity storage containers and process units.
    b. Large quantities of materials that could detonate or explode, damaging additional process units, structures, and storage containers in the immediate area.
    c. Leaks and releases that are difficult to control and could increase in size or duration.
    d. The hazardous material has been totally released from its container and is dissipating.

13. There are four critical issues that must be addressed and managed when the decision is made to commit to a full-scale public evacuation. These include:
    - Alerting and notification
    - Transportation
    - Information (keeping displaced people informed)

    What is the fourth critical issue?

SUMMARY AND REVIEW ANSWER KEY

1. Site Management is the first step in the Eight Step Process©. The major emphasis of Site Management is on establishing control of the incident scene by assuming command of the incident and isolating people from the problem by establishing an Isolation Perimeter and Hazard Control Zones. Site management and control provide the foundation for the response. Responders cannot safely and effectively implement an incident action plan (IAP) unless the playing field is clearly established and identified for both emergency responders and the public.
   For your answer to be correct, your answer should include most of the underlined words above and include a comment on safety. (p. 151)

2. The other major task of Site Management is establishing an Isolation Perimeter around the incident scene: (p. 152)

3. The other general guideline for the safe approach and position of emergency response personal at a hazmat incident is to look for physical hazmat clues, such as vapor clouds or wet areas.

4. Level II staging is used when an incident escalates past the capability of the initial response. It is a management tool usually reserved for large, complex, or lengthy hazmat operations. (p. 154)

5. b. Law enforcement or security professionals (p. 155)

6. The Incident Commander has three strategies when faced with the protection of the population: Protection-in-place, evacuation, and a combination of both. (p. 161)
7. The IC's decision to evacuate or protect-in-place (or combination) should be also based on the capability to communicate with the population at risk and emergency response personnel prior to, during, and after the emergency. (p. 162)
8. Another important factor in getting the public's compliance to protect-in-place is previous training and education by the public on the application and use of protection-in-place. (p. 165)
9. Another important variable used in evaluating structures for protection-in-place is building height. (p. 168)
10. Another condition that would call for a limited-scale evacuation is whenever explosives or reactive materials are involved and can detonate or explode, producing flying glass or structural collapse. (p. 173)
11. SBS is an abbreviation for "sick building syndrome." (p. 173)
12. d. The hazardous material has been totally released from its container and is dissipating. (p. 176 and 164)
13. The fourth critical issue that must be addressed and managed when the decision is made to commit to a full-scale public evacuation is relocation facility. (p. 177)

SELF EVALUATION

Please review all your work in this lesson. Now that you have completed this lesson, please take about 15 minutes to note your stronger and weaker areas.

Overall I feel I did (very well / well / fair / not so well) on the acronyms and abbreviations exercise.

Overall I feel I did (very well / well / fair / not so well) on the self-test questions.

Overall I feel did (very well / well / fair / not so well) on the terminology exercise.

Overall I feel I did (very well / well / fair / not so well) on the summary and review questions.

When compared to the previous lessons, I think I performed (better / worse / equally well).

List two areas in Chapter 5 in which you feel you could improve your skill or knowledge level:

1.

2.

Consider the following self-evaluation questions as they pertain to Chapter 5:

Am I taking effective margin notes?

Am I dedicating enough quality time to my studies?

Is anything distracting my focus?

Was any part of Chapter 5 too advanced for me?

Did I find that I don't have enough background experience to sufficiently grasp certain subject areas?

For areas in which I did particularly well, was it because I'm particularly interested in that subject matter? How so?

Were some things easier to learn because I have prior experience in learning or working with the concepts or principles?

Did I find that certain portions of the textbook seem to be better organized and effective in explaining key points?

What other Students have had to say about Chapter 5 material:

> "I am particularly interested in site management and control, mainly because that is one of the first areas that we all have to deal with if and when we rollup to the scene of a hazmat incident. If we allow people to walk directly into a Hot zone and we don't control the area, everything and everyone will be contaminated in a hurry and we'd have a major disaster on out hands."

> "Implementing the site management and security prior to the arrival of the hazmat team are the essential things I am involved in. The first 10 minutes of an incident, if handled properly, will contribute considerably to the successful conclusion of the incident."

> "In my position with riding the front seat of an engine, the content in this chapter can be vital. With a high probability of being the first piece in on a hazmat incident, setting up a proper site management control can be vital to the incident. Eventually the hazmat team will get to the scene and take over but until they do the situation could be in my hands."

> "As the incident commander, it is important to utilize all this information to perform effectively on scene while protecting myself, my crew members and my community."

> "Understanding the importance of establishing command, control zones, and staging areas can assist me as one of the first officers on scene."

Pat on the Back

Congratulations on working though Chapter 5 in the textbook and for completing the exercises in this lesson.

CHAPTER 6
IDENTIFY THE PROBLEM

CHAPTER ORIENTATION

Open the text to page 194. Take about 10 minutes to skim the chapter. Pay attention to the boldface subject headings. Read the titles to all the figures and note how they fit into the subject headings. Scan the case studies. Please read the introduction and summary sections carefully. When you have finished looking through Chapter 6, respond to the following items. Please use the textbook as you jot down your comments in the spaces provided below:

1. From your own experience, would you agree that a hazmat problem well defined is half-solved? Why or why not?

2. Reflect on your current level of knowledge or background experience about the topics covered in Chapter 6. Where have you read about, learned about, or applied this knowledge in the past?

3. What sections or parts of Chapter 6 strike you as looking especially interesting?

4. What particular subjects in this chapter are important for a person in your position to master?

5. What do you predict will be the hardest things for you to learn in this chapter?

LEARNING OBJECTIVES

Turn to pages 194-195 and examine the chapter objectives. When you have finished, respond to the following question:

1. Which objectives in Chapter 6 do you feel you can achieve right now, with a reasonable level of confidence?

Highlight or place a check mark next to those objectives on pages 194-195 that addresses educational competencies referenced in *NFPA 472—Professional Competence of Responders to Hazardous Materials*.

As you read the sections of the chapter that deal with the objectives you have identified above, make sure your ideas or knowledge base match those of the authors. If not, you should examine how your current understanding of the material differs from that of the authors'. Depending on the level at which you wish to master the subject, discrepancies will have to be rectified and gaps will need to be filled.

ABBREVIATIONS AND ACRONYMS

The following abbreviations and acronyms are used in Chapter 6:

AAR	Association of American Railroads (p. 213, 225, 226, 227, 228)
ANSI	American National Standards Institute (p. 202, 245)
API	American Petroleum Institute (p. 202, 231, 243, 244)
ASME	American Society of Mechanical Engineers (p. 202, 218, 234, 235, 236)
ASTM	American Society of Testing and Materials (p. 202)
CAS	Chemical Abstract Service (p. 238)
CTC	Canadian Transport Commission (p. 225)
CHEMTREC	Chemical Transportation Emergency Response Center (p. 223, 238, 255, 257)
COFC	Container on Flat Car (p. 197)

DOT	U.S. Department of Transportation (p. 202, 203, 204, 207, 211, 213, 215, 217, 218, 219, 220, 224, 225, 226, 227, 229, 238, 239, 245, 246, 247, 251, 252, 254, 255, 256, 257)
EPA	Environmental Protection Agency (p. 234, 238, 256)
ERG	Emergency Response Guidebook (p. 257)
HMT	Hazardous Materials Table (p. 245)
LC50	Lethal Concentration, 50% Kill (p. 256)
LEPC	Local Emergency Planning Committee (p. 201, 258)
LPG	Liquefied Petroleum Gas (p. 197, 215, 227, 234, 235, 236, 245)
LSA	Low Specific Activity (p. 229)
MAWP	Maximum Allowable Working Pressure (p. 215, 217, 219, 220)
N.O.S.	Not Otherwise Specified (p. 255)
NTSB	National Transportation Safety Board (p. 196)
ORM	Other Regulated Material (p. 247, 254, 257)
PG	Packing Group (p. 251, 254)
PIH	Poison—Inhalation Hazard (p, 256)
RQ	Reportable Quantity (p. 256)
SARA	Superfund Amendments and Reauthorization Act (p. 201, 258)
SCADA	Supervisory Control and Data Acquisition System (p. 241)
SCO	Surface Contaminated Objects (p. 229)
SI	International System Units (p. 252)
STCC	Standard Transportation Commodity Code (p. 257)
TC	Transport Canada (p. 225)
TI	Transport Index (p. 252, 253)
TIH	Toxic—Inhalation Hazard (p. 256)
TOFC	Trailer on Flat Car (p. 197)

Locate these abbreviations and acronyms in the textbook (page numbers provided above) and underline them. Read the paragraph in which they are used.

Fill in the blank using the abbreviations and acronyms above. Use each abbreviation or acronym only once:

1. Product flows through many transmission pipeline systems are monitored through this computerized pipeline system: ______

2. Sometimes referred to as a chemical's "social security number," these sequentially assigned numbers identify specific chemicals and have no chemical significance: ______

3. SARA Title III requires facilities to notify this entity when on-site quantities exceed established threshold values: ______

4. This federal agency requires leak detection, overfill protection, and cathode protection on underground storage tanks: ______

5. This common source of emergency response information helps first responders find emergency procedures quickly: ______

6. This classification for a chemical indicates the degree of danger associated with its transportation: ______

7. This federal agency investigated the 1971 Houston (TX) railroad derailment: ______

8. This organization focuses on bringing rail-related issues to the attention of Congressional and government leaders: ______

9. DOT regulations establish these as a class of low level radioactive waste: ______ and ______

10. This can be an indicator for determining the external radiation hazard of an undamaged package and can be a starting point for determining whether or not damage has occurred: ______

11. This record identifies the hazard class or specifies that the material is forbidden in transportation, and gives the proper shipping name or directs the user to the preferred proper shipping name: ______

12. This association has written a standard intended to establish a common system to assist in identification of hazardous materials conveyed in piping systems: ______

13. These materials do not require placards: ______

14. This seven-digit number will be found on all shipping papers accompanying rail shipments of hazmats: ______

ANSWER KEY

1. Product flows through many transmission pipeline systems are monitored through this computerized pipeline system: SCADA
2. Sometimes referred to as a chemical's "social security number," these sequentially assigned numbers identify specific chemicals and have no chemical significance: CAS
3. SARA Title III requires facilities to notify this entity when on-site quantities exceed established threshold values: LEPC
4. This federal agency requires leak detection, overfill protection, and cathode protection on underground storage tanks: EPA
5. This common source of emergency response information helps first responders find emergency procedures quickly: ERG
6. This classification for a chemical indicates the degree of danger associated with its transportation: PG
7. This federal agency investigated the 1971 Houston (TX) railroad derailment: NTSB
8. This organization focuses on bringing rail-related issues to the attention of Congressional and government leaders: AAR
9. DOT regulations establish these as a class of low level radioactive waste: SCO and LSA

10. This can be an indicator for determining the external radiation hazard of an undamaged package and can be a starting point for determining whether or not damage has occurred: TI

11. This record identifies the hazard class or specifies that the material is forbidden in transportation, and gives the proper shipping name or directs the user to the preferred proper shipping name: HMT

12. This association has written a standard intended to establish a common system to assist in identification of hazardous materials conveyed in piping systems: ANSI

13. These materials do not require placards: ORM

14. This seven-digit number will be found on all shipping papers accompanying rail shipments of hazmats: STCC

STUDY SESSION OVERVIEW

Read pages 196 to the top of page 229, then take a short break to think about what you have read. Then read the rest of the chapter. Take margin notes as you go. Underline or highlight phrases that you feel are important.

When you have completed your reading, respond to the following questions. You may use the textbook to help you answer the questions, or work from memory.

1. Based on your current understanding of problem identification, explain why problem identification cannot be safely accomplished if responders have not first controlled the incident scene.

2. What is the primary lesson-learned from the 1971 Houston (TX) railroad derailment and explosion?

3. Based on your current understanding of hazardous materials response, what is the rationale behind the statement: "If you can't identify, then try to classify." (p. 199)

4. Explain the relationship between distance and exposure risk when selecting an identification method (clues).

SELF-TEST

Answer the following questions. You may use the textbook to help you answer the questions, or work from memory.

1. The identification process has three basic elements – recognition, identification, and: [p. 199]
   a. Classification
   b. Verification
   c. Detection
   d. Description

2. Which of the following occupancies and locations is a potential hazmat site: [p. 201]
   a. Water treatment plant
   b. Railroad tank car
   c. Residential apartment
   d. All of the above

3. Packaging used for transporting hazardous materials is regulated by: [p. 202]
   a. American Petroleum Institute (API)
   b. ASME, ASTM, and ANSI
   c. Dept. of Transportation (DOT)
   d. NFPA 30

4. The following are all examples of nonbulk packaging, except one: [p. 203]
   a. Ton container
   b. Drum
   c. Carboy
   d. Glass bottles inside a fiberboard box

5. Bulk packaging is any packaging that meets one the following definitions: [p. 203]
   a. Liquid capacity greater than 500 gallons
   b. Solid net mass greater than one ton
   c. Compressed gas water capacity greater than 1,001 pound
   d. An integral part of a transport vehicle (e.g., cargo tank truck)

6. Which of the following is an example of a facility containment system: [p. 204]
   a. Storage bins or cabinets
   b. Buildings
   c. Piping
   d. All of the above

7. Of the following materials, which is most likely to be found in a nonbulk bag: [p. 205]
   a. Radioactive materials
   b. Caustic powders
   c. Solvents
   d. Infectious disease samples

8. Which of the following would <u>not</u> be found in an aluminum drum: [p. 206]
   a. Materials that react with rust
   b. Combustible materials
   c. Caustic corrosives
   d. Pesticides

9. Almost any hazmat can be found inside a box, excluding: [p. 207]
   a. Laboratory reagents
   b. Poisons
   c. Compressed gases
   d. Organic peroxides

10. Of the following materials, which is most likely to be found in a nonbulk carboy: [p. 208]
    a. Corrosive liquids
    b. Non-flammable pressurized gases
    c. Cryogenic liquids
    d. Explosives

11. Which of the following bulk packaging would contain liquefied gases, including chlorine: [p. 210]
    a. Super sacks
    b. Ton containers
    c. Polyethylene and steel tanks
    d. Portable bins

12. A DOT Spec 51 pressure tank container is most likely to contain: [p. 213]
    a. Food grade commodities
    b. Cryogenic liquids
    c. Alcohols
    d. Pyrophoric liquids

13. Service pressures ranging up to 2,400 psi and higher are characteristic of: [p. 216]
   a. Tube modules
   b. IMO Type 7 tanks
   c. IM 101 tanks
   d. IM 105 tanks

14. A DOT-406 AL specification indicates that the cargo tank is: [p. 217]
   a. A DOT-406 inspected annually
   b. A DOT -406 manufactured prior to 1990
   c. A DOT -406 constructed of aluminum
   d. A DOT -406 registered in Alabama

Match each cargo tank truck in Column A to its specification type in Column B.

Column A **Cargo Tank Truck**	**Column B** **Contents/Hazard Class**
15.______Atmospheric pressure cargo tank truck (p. 219)	A. MC 330/MC-331
16.______Low pressure chemical cargo tank truck (p. 219)	B. MC-306/DOT-406
17.______Corrosive cargo tank truck (p. 220)	C. MC-338
18.______High pressure cargo tank truck (p. 220)	D. MC-312/DOT-412
19.______Cryogenic liquid cargo tank truck (p. 221)	E. MC-307/DOT-407

20. Heated material cargo tank trucks are required to be placarded as: [p. 222]
   a. "HOT" material
   b. "Dangerous" material
   c. "Combustible" material
   d. "Molten Liquid" material

21. Reporting marks and number (e.g. GATX 12345) can be used to obtain information about: [p. 223]
   a. The contents of the car
   b. The tank car's test pressure
   c. The type of material used in tank construction
   d. The builder's name, tank specification, and class designation

Match each railroad tank car in Column A to the materials it carries, listed in Column B.

Column A **Railroad Tank Car**	**Column B** **Contents/Hazard Class**
22.______Non-pressure tank car (p. 226)	A. Liquid oxygen, liquid hydrogen, liquid argon, etc.
23.______Pressure tank car (p. 227)	B. Liquid poisons, organic peroxides, vegetable oils
24.______Cryogenic liquid tank car (p. 227)	C. Chlorine, anhydrous ammonia, LPG
25.______Pneumatically unloaded covered hopper car (p. 228)	D. Pellets, caustic flake, resin powder, flour, etc.

26. Most low level radioactive waste, such as contaminated protective clothing, is shipped in: [p. 229]
    a. Excepted packaging
    b. Industrial packaging
    c. Type A packaging
    d. Type B packaging

27. Potentially life-endangering amounts of radioactive material, such as spent nuclear fuel, that could pose a significant risk if released during an accident are transported in: [p. 230]
    a. Excepted packaging
    b. Industrial packaging
    c. Type A packaging
    d. Type B packaging

28. The most common storage tank found in the petroleum industry is the: [p. 232]
    a. Cone roof tank
    b. Covered floating roof tank
    c. Open floating roof tank
    d. Open floating roof tank with geodesic dome

29. At chemical facilities, underground storage tanks may store: [p. 234]
    a. Only combustible liquids
    b. Only liquefied petroleum gases
    c. Flammable and non-flammable liquefied gases
    d. Virtually any hazardous or non-hazardous liquid

30. The signal words found on agricultural chemicals and pesticide container labels indicate: [p. 237]
    a. Level of toxicity
    b. Concentration
    c. Ratio of active to inert ingredients
    d. Hazard class

31. Which of the following is the only reliable way to identify cylinder contents: [p. 238]
    a. Color codes
    b. CAS number
    c. Product information stencil
    d. DOT label attached to the cylinder head

32. Pipeline markers must provide the pipeline contents, the pipeline operator, and: [p. 241]
    a. Four-digit identification number
    b. Emergency telephone number
    c. CAS number
    d. DOT hazard class

33. The yellow quadrant in the NFPA 704 marking system indicates: [p. 242]
    a. PCBs
    b. Reactivity
    c. Toxicity
    d. Radioactivity

34. The hazmat placarding and labeling requirements within the U.S. are regulated by the: [p. 245]
    a. EPA
    b. API
    c. DOT
    d. OSHA

35. Placards that are applied to freight containers, cargo tanks, and portable tank containers are approximately ______ in size: [p. 246]
    a. 4 inches square
    b. 11 inches square
    c. 18 inches square
    d. 24 inches square

36. Transport container with two or more categories of hazmats that require different placards specified in Table 2 *may* be placarded with a __________ placard instead of the specific placards required for each of the Table 2 materials: [p. 251]
    a. DANGEROUS
    b. WARNING
    c. CAUTION
    d. Skull and crossbones

37. A package with a radioactive White-I label will (normally) contain: [p. 253]
    a. Fissile Class III materials
    b. Materials rated at a maximum allowable TI = 1
    c. Materials with high radiation levels
    d. Materials with extremely low or almost no levels of radiation

38. The Packing Group entry on shipping papers indicates:
[p. 254]
   a. Type of packaging
   b. Degree of danger
   c. Hazard class
   d. Hazardous waste classification

39. Shipping papers must include the following emergency response information:
[p. 257]
   a. Personnel protective measures
   b. First aid measures
   c. Emergency actions involving fire
   d. All of the above

ANSWER KEY

Check your answers. If you missed more than ten, you should read the chapter once again.

1. The identification process has three basic elements – recognition, identification, and:
[p. 199]
   a. Classification
   b. Verification
   c. Detection
   d. Description

2. Which of the following occupancies and locations is a potential hazmat site:
[p. 201]
   a. Water treatment plant
   b. Railroad tank car
   c. Residential apartment
   d. All of the above

3. Packaging used for transporting hazardous materials is regulated by:
[p. 202]
   a. American Petroleum Institute (API)
   b. ASME, ASTM, and ANSI
   c. Dept. of Transportation (DOT)
   d. NFPA 30

4. The following are all examples of nonbulk packaging, except one:
[p. 203]
   a. Ton container
   b. Drum
   c. Carboy
   d. Glass bottles inside a fiberboard box

5. Bulk packaging is any packaging that meets one the following definitions:
[p. 203]
   a. Liquid capacity greater than 500 gallons

b. Solid net mass greater than one ton
c. Compressed gas water capacity greater than 1,001 pound
d. An integral part of a transport vehicle (e.g., cargo tank truck)

6. Which of the following is an example of a facility containment system:
[p. 204]
a. Storage bins or cabinets
b. Buildings
c. Piping
d. All of the above

7. Of the following materials, which is most likely to be found in a nonbulk bag:
[p. 205]
a. Radioactive materials
b. Caustic powders
c. Solvents
d. Infectious disease samples

8. Which of the following would not be found in an aluminum drum:
[p. 206]
a. Materials that react with rust
b. Combustible materials
c. Caustic corrosives
d. Pesticides

9. Almost any hazmat can be found inside a box, excluding:
[p. 207]
a. Laboratory reagents
b. Poisons
c. Compressed gases
d. Organic peroxides

10. Of the following materials, which is most likely to be found in a nonbulk carboy:
[p. 208]
a. Corrosive liquids
b. Non-flammable pressurized gases
c. Cryogenic liquids
d. Explosives

11. Which of the following bulk paging would contain liquefied gases, including chlorine:
[p. 210]
a. Super sacks
b. Ton containers
c. Polyethylene and steel tanks
d. Portable bins

12. A DOT Spec 51 pressure tank container is most likely to contain:
[p. 213]
a. Food grade commodities
b. Cryogenic liquids
c. Alcohols
d. Pyrophoric liquids

13. Service pressures ranging up to 2,400 psi and higher are characteristic of: [p. 216]
    <u>a</u>. **Tube modules**
    b. IMO Type 7 tanks
    c. IM 101 tanks
    d. IM 105 tanks

14. A DOT-406 AL specification indicates that the cargo tank is: [p. 217]
    a. A DOT-406 inspected annually
    b. A DOT-406 manufactured prior to 1990
    <u>c</u>. **A DOT-406 constructed of aluminum**
    d. A DOT-406 registered in Alabama

Match each cargo tank truck in Column A to its specification type in Column B.

Column A Cargo Tank Truck	Column B Contents/Hazard Class
15.__B__Atmospheric pressure cargo tank truck (p. 219)	A. MC 330/MC-331
16.__E__Low pressure chemical cargo tank truck (p. 219)	B. MC-306/DOT-406
17.__D__Corrosive cargo tank truck (p. 220)	C. MC-338
18.__A__High pressure cargo tank truck (p. 220)	D. MC-312/DOT-412
19.__C__Cryogenic liquid cargo tank truck (p. 221)	E. MC-307/DOT-407

20. Heated material cargo tank trucks are required to be placarded as: [p. 222]
    <u>a</u>. **"HOT" material**
    b. "Dangerous" material
    c. "Combustible" material
    d. "Molten Liquid" material

21. Reporting marks and number (e.g. GATX 12345) can be used to obtain information about: [p. 223]
    <u>a</u>. **The contents of the car**
    b. The tank car's test pressure
    c. The type of material used in tank construction
    d. The builder's name, tank specification, and class designation

Match each railroad tank car in Column A to the materials it carries, listed in Column B.

Column A Railroad Tank Car	Column B Contents/Hazard Class
22. __B__ Non-pressure tank car (p. 226)	A. Liquid oxygen, liquid hydrogen, liquid argon, etc.
23. __C__ Pressure tank car (p. 227)	B. Liquid poisons, organic peroxides, vegetable oils
24. __A__ Cryogenic liquid tank car (p. 227)	C. Chlorine, anhydrous ammonia, LPG
25. __D__ Pneumatically unloaded covered hopper car (p. 228)	D. Pellets, caustic flake, resin powder, flour, etc.

26. Most low level radioactive waste, such as contaminated protective clothing, is shipped in: [p. 229]
    a. Excepted packaging
    b. Industrial packaging
    c. Type A packaging
    d. Type B packaging

27. Potentially life-endangering amounts of radioactive material, such as spent nuclear fuel, that could pose a significant risk if released during an accident are transported in: [p. 230]
    a. Excepted packaging
    b. Industrial packaging
    c. Type A packaging
    d. Type B packaging

28. The most common storage tank found in the petroleum industry is the: [p. 232]
    a. Cone roof tank
    b. Covered floating roof tank
    c. Open floating roof tank
    d. Open floating roof tank with geodesic dome

29. At chemical facilities, underground storage tanks may store: [p. 234]
    a. Only combustible liquids
    b. Only liquefied petroleum gases
    c. Flammable and non-flammable liquefied gases
    d. Virtually any hazardous or non-hazardous liquid

30. The signal words found on agricultural chemicals and pesticide container labels indicate: [p. 237]
    a. Level of toxicity
    b. Concentration
    c. Ratio of active to inert ingredients
    d. Hazard class

31. Which of the following is the only reliable way to identify cylinder contents: [p. 238]

a. Color codes
b. CAS number
c. Product information stencil
d. DOT label attached to the cylinder head

32. Pipeline markers must provide the pipeline contents, the pipeline operator, and:
[p. 241]
a. Four-digit identification number
b. Emergency telephone number
c. CAS number
d. DOT hazard clas

33. The yellow quadrant in the NFPA 704 marking system indicates:
[p. 242]
a. PCBs
b. Reactivity
c. Toxicity
d. Radioactivity

34. The hazmat placarding and labeling requirements within the U.S. are regulated by the:
[p. 245]
a. EPA
b. API
c. DOT
d. OSHA

35. Placards that are applied to freight containers, cargo tanks, and portable tank containers are approximately ______ in size:
[p. 246]
a. 4 inches square
b. 11 inches square
c. 18 inches square
d. 24 inches square

36. Transport container with two or more categories of hazmats that require different placards specified in Table 2 *may* be placarded with a __________ placard instead of the specific placards required for each of the Table 2 materials:
[p. 251]
a. DANGEROUS
b. WARNING
c. CAUTION
d. Skull and crossbones

37. A package with a radioactive White-I label will (normally) contain:
[p. 253]
a. Fissile Class III materials
b. Materials rated at a maximum allowable TI = 1
c. Materials with high radiation levels
d. Materials with extremely low or almost no levels of radiation

38. The Packing Group entry on shipping papers indicates:
[p. 254]
   a. Type of packaging
   b. Degree of danger
   c. Hazard class
   d. Hazardous waste classification

39. Shipping papers must include the following emergency response information:
[p. 257]
   a. Personnel protective measures
   b. First aid measures
   c. Emergency actions involving fire
   d. All of the above

PRACTICE

1. Obtain a copy of the latest DOT Emergency Response Guidebook (ERG) (print or online version). Practice using the ERG to identify hazardous materials by identification number:

DOT#	Chemical Name:
1051	
1256	
1114	
1075	
2055	
2810	
1198	
2790	
1050	
1972	
1760	
1079	
1203	
1282	
1005	

2. Locate an online CAS Registry Number Search service (at the time of this writing, there are a number of such services such as the one offered by NIST, http://webbook.nist.gov/chemistry/cas-ser.html). Practice using the CAS Number to identify hazardous materials:

CAS#	Chemical Name:
506-77-4	
8030-30-6	
8014-95-7	
7664-38-2	
1310-73-2	

5. Go to http://www.8stepprocess.com for additional information and activities pertaining to Chapter 6 "Identify the Problem."

STUDY GROUP ACTIVITY

Working with a partner, take a few field trips to various industries within your community, as well as to railroad yards and pipeline crossover locations. Identify the marking systems used, and practice locating and interpreting the information provided by the markings. Use a small notebook to record your observations. Which ones are the easiest to locate and interpret? Which ones are the most difficult, or provide the least useful information for emergency responders? Discuss your experiences with your study group.

STUDY GROUP LEARNING THROUGH INQUIRY SCENARIO 6-1

You are the Fire Marshal within your community. The Local Emergency Planning Committee (LEPC) has proposed an ordinance to the local elected officials that a facility marking system be implemented for all SARA Title III reporting facilities within the community. The primary objective of this system would be to allow emergency responders to (1) identify those facilities which manufacture, store, handle and use hazardous materials within the community, and (2) allow emergency responders to become more familiar with such facilities.

Although the Fire Chief favors the proposal because of firefighter health and safety concerns, the Police Chief has raised some substantive security issues with respect to identifying such facilities to the public. The Police Chief points out that hazardous materials stored at legitimate and legal facilities can be broken into and used to make an explosive device or as feedstock to make illegal drugs. Facilities could also be accessed during a riot. Why make it easier for the "Bad Guys" by telling them where the hazmat is stored?

The Fire Chief has turned the LEPC's proposal over to you and is now awaiting your recommendations and suggestions as to how the fire department should pursue the issue. He makes it clear that he wants a marking system that will improve firefighter safety. He also makes it clear that he has worked hard to develop a good working relationship with the Police Chief and he wants to be responsive to the Police Chief's concerns. Any recommendation that you develop must address the security concerns.

Using the limited background information provided and the information discussed in Chapter 6, answer the following questions:

1) What "off the shelf" nationally recognized systems are available which could be adopted? What would be the advantages and disadvantages of adopting one system over another? (Review pages 242 to 245, Chapter 6.)
2) How can the facility marking system program be implemented from a safety perspective while minimizing the security concerns expressed by the Police Department?
3) Assuming that you believe the firefighter safety benefits of implementing a marking system far outweigh the negative aspects from a security point of view, how would make your case to the Police Chief?

STUDY GROUP LEARNING THROUGH INQUIRY SCENARIO 6-2

You are the Incident Commander at the scene of a tractor trailer incident involving a leaking unknown liquid substance. It is approximately 4:00 PM on a cold February weekday. The incident was reported by the truck driver who noticed liquid leaking from his truck through his rear view mirror while driving down the interstate highway. The driver pulled off the interstate and parked his vehicle on a side street in a heavily congested area and dialed 911 for assistance.

Your HMRT has isolated the immediate area and interviewed the driver who is very cooperative but has limited knowledge of his cargo. The manifest shows that the truck contains fifty-seven (57) - 55-gallon drums of mixed hazardous waste. Most of the drums contain different pesticide solutions.

After evaluating the hazards and risk, you decide to send a recon team to the truck to inspect the vehicle and recover a sample. As a precaution, you have decided to evacuate several nearby stores. The owners are very unhappy about this since 5:00 PM to 7:00 PM is their best sales period.

While this operation is being conducted, several TV news vehicles show up and meet with your PIO. They indicate that they will be going live for the 6 o'clock news broadcast. The time is about 5:30 PM. You agree to have your PIO conduct a preliminary press briefing, however, you inform the PIO that recent hazmat incidents along the interstate highway corridor have generated many citizen complaints concerning the need to close down the highway. There is a great deal of local sensitivity to this issue and he should anticipate that questions might be raised during the interviews.

After conducting the first press briefing, your recon team reports that the leaking liquid appears to be water, which is melting from ice trapped on the top of the hazardous waste drums. A sample tested on the scene using a HazCat® Kit confirms that the leaking liquid is in fact uncontaminated water.

Based on the background information provided and the information in Chapter 6, answer the following questions:

1) What methods of identification should be available to the HMRT on this incident which would help confirm that the cargo is hazardous waste? How could the HMRT identify the constituents of the individual hazardous waste drums?

2) How would you brief the media on this issue if you conducted the interview before you learned that the material leaking was water? What are the three key points you would want to make in your briefing?

3) Assuming that you already briefed the media once (question 2 above) how would you brief the media after you discovered that the leaking material was water? Would you specifically tell the media that the material was water and not hazardous waste?

4) How do you think this would look to the general public if the evacuation issue was raised by a reporter on live television? You justified the need to evacuate and block roads in the first interview, now it turns out that you took this action for leaking water! Isn't this just another case of the fire department over reacting to the problem?

SUMMARY AND REVIEW

1. Where do most hazardous materials releases occur, in facilities or during transportation?

2. List at least three basic recognition clues (e.g., occupancy and location):

3. Identify those clues can be used to identify possible weapons of mass destruction:

4. Of the various identification methods, which one poses the highest risk to responders? Why?

5. Which federal organization regulates packaging used for transporting hazardous materials?

6. Packing is divided into three general groups—

   1) Nonbulk packaging

   2) ______________

   3) ______________

7. What are overpack drums used for?

8. In what facilities are carboys typically found, and what can be found inside them?

9. In what type of cylinder are cryogenic liquids found?

10. You locate a cylindrical pressure tank approximately 3 feet in diameter and 8 feet long with concave heads, on a transport vehicle. What type of container is this and what is its likely contents/hazard class?

11. You locate a polyethylene tank inside of a rigid steel frame, with a top tank fill opening and top or bottom discharge piping. What type of container is this and what is its likely contents/hazard class?

12. You locate a tank container consisting of seamless steel cylinders from 9 to 48-inches in diameter, permanently mounted inside an open frame. A box-like compartment at one end encloses all the valves. What are its likely contents?

13. What does the capacity stencil on a railroad tank car tell you?

14. Which of the following radioactive material packaging is <u>not</u> designed to withstand the forces of an accident:
   a. Excepted packaging
   b. Industrial packaging
   c. Type A packaging
   d. Type B packaging

15. There are three ways to positively identify a pesticide. One way is by product name. What are the other two ways:

16. What is the purpose of four digit identification numbers:

17. Placards and labels provide recognition and general hazard classification by way of four indicators:

   1) Colored background

   2)

   3)

   4)

18. Three different labels are used on radioactive material packaging:

   1) Radioactive White–I

   2)

   3)

19. If the airbill is not attached to the outside of packages being transported by air, where should you look for it?

20. True or False: All shipping papers must contain an emergency response telephone number.

SUMMARY AND REVIEW ANSWER KEY

1. Studies show that approximately 75% of releases occur in facilities that produce, store, manufacture, or use chemicals; the remaining 25% occur during transportation. (p. 197)

2. To be correct, your answer should include at least three of the following:
   - Container shapes
   - Markings and colors
   - Placards and labels
   - Shipping and facility documents
   - Monitoring and detection equipment
   - Senses (p. 198)

3. Identify those clues that can be used to identify possible weapons of mass destruction:
   - Occupancy and location
   - Container shapes
   - Monitoring and detection equipment (p. 199)

4. Monitoring and detection equipment. The closer you are to the problem when identifying the hazmat(s) involved, the greater your risk of exposure (p. 200)

5. Department of Transportation (DOT) (p. 202)

6. The other groups are bulking packaging and facility containment systems (p. 203)

7. Overpack drums are used for transporting damaged or leaking nonbulk containers of all types and sizes. Range from lab packs to 85-gallon overpacks. (p. 206)

8. Carboys are typically found in laboratories and chemical manufacturing facilities. They can contain liquids, including flammable and combustible liquids, and corrosives. (p. 208)

9. Cryogenic (insulated) cylinders and Dewars containers. (p. 209)

10. Ton container. Contains liquefied gases, including chlorine, sulfur dioxide, and phosgene. (p. 210) Note correction to Fig. 6.13. Convex=refrigerant gases; Concave= chlorine and phosgene.

11. "Tote," an intermediate bulk container (IBC). Contains liquid materials, including corrosives and Class 9 materials. (p. 211)

12. Pressurized gases, such as oxygen, hydrogen, nitrogen, and helium. (p. 216)

13. The capacity stencil shows the volume of a tank car in gallons (and sometimes in liters), as well as in pounds (and sometimes kilograms). (p. 224)

14. c. Type A packaging (p. 229)

15. The other two ways are:

    - Chemical ingredient statement
    - EPA registration number (p. 238)

16. They are used to determine the name of the material and to obtain hazard and response information from emergency response guidebooks. (p. 239)

17. The other three indicators are:

    - Respective hazard class symbol
    - Hazard class/division number
    - Hazard class description wording or the four-digit identification number (found in the center of the placard) (p. 246)

18. The other two labels are: Radioactive Yellow–II and Radioactive Yellow–III. (p. 252)

19. Airbills are located in cockpit (p. 254)

20. True (p. 255)

SELF EVALUATION

Please review all your work in this lesson. Now that you have completed this lesson, please take about 15 minutes to note your stronger and weaker areas.

Overall I feel I did (very well / well / fair / not so well) on the acronyms and abbreviations exercise.

Overall I feel I did (very well / well / fair / not so well) on the self-test questions.

Overall I feel I did (very well / well / fair / not so well) on the summary and review questions.

When compared to the previous lessons, I think I performed (better / worse / equally well).

List two areas in Chapter 6 in which you feel you could improve your skill or knowledge level:

1.

2.

Consider the following self-evaluation questions as they pertain to Chapter 6:

Am I taking effective margin notes?

Am I dedicating enough quality time to my studies?

Is anything distracting my focus?

Was any part of Chapter 6 too advanced for me?

Did I find that I don't have enough background experience to sufficiently grasp certain subject areas?

For areas in which I did particularly well, was it because I'm particularly interested in that subject matter? How so?

Were some things easier to learn because I have prior experience in learning or working with the concepts or principles?

Did I find that certain portions of the textbook seem to be better organized and effective in explaining key points?

What other Students have had to say about Chapter 6 material:

> "I've taken many hazmat classes over the years, and one thing that seems to stay the same is the container shapes, colors, and marking.
>
> As a company officer, my decisions and actions will have a dramatic impact on the outcome of the incident. An improper identification of the cargo could lead to not only the demise of my crew, but many people in the path of the hazard. With this in mind, identification of the hazard is of paramount importance.
>
> I feel that it is very important as a line officer to be able to recognize, identify, and classify a hazmat incident. These three steps are needed to be completed quickly at a hazmat incident. It is important for a line officer to complete these task because many of times the engine will be the first arriving on a hazmat incident.
>
> Recognition, identification, and classification is something I definitely can use more training on. Understanding how to read shipping papers or identify placards on containers is crucial to realizing whether a threat actually exists and how severe it may be."

Pat on the Back

Congratulations on working though Chapter 6 in the textbook and for completing the exercises in this lesson.

CHAPTER 7

HAZARD ASSESSMENT AND RISK EVALUATION

CHAPTER ORIENTATION

Open the text to page 266. Take about 10 minutes to skim the chapter. Pay attention to the boldface subject headings. Read the titles to all the figures and note how they fit into the subject headings. Scan the case studies. Please read the introduction and summary sections carefully. When you have finished looking through Chapter 7, respond to the following items. Please use the textbook as you jot down your comments in the spaces provided below:

1. Stated as simply as possible, what is the object of hazard and risk evaluation?

2. Reflect on your current level of knowledge or background experience about the topics covered in Chapter 7. Where have you read about, learned about, or applied this knowledge in the past?

3. What sections or parts of Chapter 7 strike you as looking especially interesting?

4. What particular subjects in this chapter are important for a person in your position to master?

5. What do you predict will be the hardest things for you to learn in this chapter?

LEARNING OBJECTIVES

Turn to pages, 266-267 and examine the chapter objectives. When you have finished, respond to the following question:

1. Which objectives in Chapter 7 do you feel you can achieve right now, with a reasonable level of confidence?

Highlight or place a check mark next to those objectives on pages 38-39 that addresses educational competencies referenced in *NFPA 472—Professional Competence of Responders to Hazardous Materials.*

As you read the sections of the chapter that deal with the objectives you have identified above, make sure your ideas or knowledge base match those of the authors. If not, you should examine how your current understanding of the material differs from that of the authors'. Depending on the level at which you wish to master the subject, discrepancies will have to be rectified and gaps will need to be filled.

ABBREVIATIONS AND ACRONYMS

The following abbreviations and acronyms are used in Chapter 7:

ACC	American Chemistry Council (p. 287)
ALOHA	Aerial Locations of Hazardous Atmospheres (p. 290, 327)
ATSDR	Agency for Toxic Substances and Disease Registry (p. 288)
CAMEO	Computer Assisted Management of Emergency Operations (p. 289, 290, 327)
CANUTEC	Canadian Transport Emergency Centre (p. 288)
CEPPO	Chemical Emergency Prevention and Preparedness Office (EPA) (p. 289, 290)
CHEMNET	Chemical Industry Mutual Aid Network (p. 287)
CHEMTREC	Chemical Transportation Emergency Center (p. 287, 288, 290)
cpm	Counts per Minute (p. 298, 299, 312)
eV	Electron Volts (p. 302, 303, 307)

FT-IR	Fourier Transform Infrared Spectrometry (p. 304, 313)
FOG	Field Operations Guide (p. 284)
GC	Gas Chromatograph (p. 303)
GHBMO	General Hazardous Materials Emergency Behavior Model (p. 319)
IP	Ionization Potential (p. 286, 302, 303)
LEPC	Local Emergency Planning Committee (p. 289)
MARPLOT	Mapping Applications for Response, Planning and Local Operational Tasks (p. 289, 290)
MS	Mass Spectrometer (p. 303)
MSST	Maximum Safe Storage Temperature (p. 279)
NAPCC	National Animal Poison Control Center (p. 288, 289)
NEC	National Electrical Code (p. 295)
NPIC	National Pesticide Information Center (p. 289)
NTSB	National Transportation Safety Board (p. 270, 319)
pH	Power of Hydrogen (p. 279, 298, 305, 311, 312)
PID	Photo-Ionization Detector (p. 302, 303, 307)
RQ	Reportable Quantity (p. 288)
SADT	Self-Accelerating Decomposition Temperature (p. 279)
SETIQ	Mexican Emergency Transportation System for the Chemical Industry (p. 288)
UV	Ultraviolet (p. 302)

Locate these abbreviations and acronyms in the textbook (page numbers provided above) and underline them. Read the paragraph in which they are used.

For each of the following sentences, write in the correct abbreviation or acronym (from the list above) so that that sentence makes sense. Use each abbreviation or acronym only once:

1. There are two primary ionizing detectors used in the field: the flame ionization detector and the _______.

2. Flame ionization detectors operate in to modes: the survey mode and the _______ mode.

3. The _______ is usually coupled with a gas chromatograph and is the identifying portion of the device.

4. _______ technology allows for the specific identification of liquid and solid samples.

5. Radiation survey instruments read in _______.

6. The _______ scale ranges from 0 to 14.

7. Irreversible decomposition of an organic peroxide begins when the _______ is reached.

8. The _______ is used to plot releases of hazardous materials vapors.

9. When using a photo-ionization detector, the sample is exposed to a _______ lamp which ionizes the sample.

Match each agency abbreviation in Column A to its description in Column B.

Column A Agency	**Column B Description**
10.______SETIQ (p. 288)	A. The leading federal public health agency for hazmat incidents.
11.______ACC (p. 287)	B. Provides assistance in identification and establishing contact with shippers and manufacturers of hazardous materials that originate in Canada.
12.______CHEMNET (p. 287)	C. Provides consultation in the diagnosis and treatment of suspected or actual animal poisonings or chemical contamination and staffs an emergency response team to investigate such incidents.
13.______ATSDR (p. 288)	D. A service of the Mexico National Association of Chemical Industries
14.______CANUTEC (p. 288)	E. This federal agency investigates transportation accidents and promulgates safety recommendations.
15.______CHEMTREC (p. 287)	F. Operates CHEMTREC, the most recognized emergency information center in the U.S.
16.______CEPPO (p. 290)	G. Provides information on pesticide-related health/toxicity questions, properties, and minor clean-up to physicians, veterinarians, responders, and the general public.
17.______NAPCC (p. 288-289)	H. Provides a number of emergency and non-emergency services, including emergency response information and emergency communications.
18.______NPIC (p. 289)	I. The chemical industry mutual aid network under contract to ACC.
19.______NTSB (p. 270)	J. An organization within the EPA that provides a good starting point for gathering hazard information.

ANSWER KEY

1. There are two primary ionizing detectors used in the field: the flame ionization detector and the PID.
2. Flame ionization detectors operate in to modes: the survey mode and the GC mode.
3. The MS is usually coupled with a gas chromatograph and is the identifying portion of the device.
4. FT-IR technology allows for the specific identification of liquid and solid samples.

5. Radiation survey instruments read in CMP.

6. The pH scale ranges from 0 to 14.

7. Irreversible decomposition of an organic peroxide begins when the SADT is reached.

8. The ALOHA is used to plot releases of hazardous materials vapors.

9. When using a photo-ionization detector, the sample is exposed to a UV lamp which ionizes the sample.

Match each agency abbreviation in Column A to its description in Column B.

Column A Agency	Column B Description
10. __D__ SETIQ (p. 288)	A. The leading federal public health agency for hazmat incidents.
11. __F__ ACC (p. 287)	B. Provides assistance in identification and establishing contact with shippers and manufacturers of hazardous materials that originate in Canada.
12. __I__ CHEMNET (p. 287)	C. Provides consultation in the diagnosis and treatment of suspected or actual animal poisonings or chemical contamination and staffs an emergency response team to investigate such incidents.
13. __A__ ATSDR (p. 288)	D. A service of the Mexico National Association of Chemical Industries
14. __B__ CANUTEC (p. 288)	E. This federal agency investigates transportation accidents and promulgates safety recommendations.
15. __H__ CHEMTREC (p. 287)	F. Operates CHEMTREC, the most recognized emergency information center in the U.S.
16. __J__ CEPPO (p. 290)	G. Provides information on pesticide-related health/toxicity questions, properties, and minor clean-up to physicians, veterinarians, responders, and the general public.
17. __C__ NAPCC (p. 288-289)	H. Provides a number of emergency and non-emergency services, including emergency response information and emergency communications.
18. __G__ NPIC (p. 289)	I. The chemical industry mutual aid network under contract to ACC.
19. __E__ NTSB (p. 270)	J. An organization within the EPA that provides a good starting point for gathering hazard information.

STUDY SESSION OVERVIEW

Read pages 266 to the top of page 317, then take a short break to think about what you have read. Then read the rest of the chapter. Take margin notes as you go. Underline or highlight phrases that you feel are important.

When you have completed your reading, respond to the following questions. You may use the textbook to help you answer the questions, or work from memory.

1. Based upon what you have read in this chapter and have previously learned about hazardous materials incident management, how might the outcome of the 1989 hazmat train derailment (see page 270 in the text) been different had the IC played a more active role during the hazard and risk assessment process?

2. In your own words, define what a hazard is and provide several examples.

3. Next, define risk. Why can't we evaluate risk based solely on a knowledge and understanding of the hazards involved?

4. Which of the hazard data and information sources (begins on page 281) do you have the most experience with? Which ones would you like to become more familiar with?

5. The "Rule of Threes" means using several types of detection technologies to classify or identify the hazard. What is the rationale for this practice?

6. In your own words, explain why defensive tactics are always preferable over offensive tactics if they can accomplish the same objectives in a timely manner.

7. What is the nonintervention mode and when is it ideally implemented?

SELF-TEST

Answer the following questions. You may use the textbook to help you answer the questions, or work from memory.

1. The temperature of a material within its container is called the:
   [p. 274]
   a. Ambient temperature
   b. Normal physical state
   c. Temperature of product
   d. Critical temperature

2. Which of the following properties is the most significant for evaluating spill control options and clean-up procedures for waterborne releases:
   [p. 274]

a. Specific gravity
b. Boiling point
c. Vapor pressure
d. Concentration

3. Critical temperature and critical pressure are both terms that relate to:
[p. 276]
a. The distance that gases and vapors will travel
b. The process of liquefying gases
c. The evaluation of flammability hazards of a material
d. The point at which the vapor pressure of a liquid equals atmospheric pressure

4. Miscibility is the ability of materials to:
[p. 277]
a. Float on water
b. Absorb into a permeable solid
c. Dissolve into a uniform mixture
d. Change chemically into another substance

5. Which of the following is most significant in determining the temperature at which the vapors from a flammable liquid are readily available and may ignite:
[p. 277]
a. Flash point
b. Fire point
c. Maximum safe storage temperature (MSST)
d. Self-accelerating decomposition temperature (SADT)

6. The percentage of an acid or based dissolved in water is called the:
[p. 279]
a. Strength
b. pH
c. Water reactivity
d. Concentration

7. Another term for caustic is:
[p. 279]
a. Air reactive
b. Corrosive
c. Acid
d. Base

8. The time it takes for the activity of a radioactive material to decrease to one half of its initial value through radioactive decay is called the:
[p. 280]
a. Dose
b. Dose rate
c. Half-dose
d. Half-life

9. Chemical warfare agents such as tabun, sarin, soman, and VX are all examples of:
[p. 280]

a. Nerve agents
b. Choking agents
c. Vesicants (blister agents)
d. Pathogens

10. Which of the following terms refers to the length of time a chemical agent remains as a liquid:
[p. 280]
a. Strength
b. Activity
c. Persistence
d. Oxidation ability

11. All of the guidebooks and manuals listed in Figure 7.4 are written for a target audience of:
[p. 283-286]
a. First Responders—Awareness and Operations levels
b. Hazardous Materials Technicians and Specialists
c. Incident Commanders
d. Product Specialists

12. Which of the following agencies is the federal government's central reporting point for all oil, chemical, radiological, biological, and etiological releases into the environment within the US and its territories:
[p. 288]
a. EPA Chemical Emergency Preparedness and Prevention Office (CEPPO)
b. Department of Transportation National Response Center (NRC)
c. Federal Emergency Management Agency (FEMA)
d. U.S. Chemical Safety and Hazard Investigation Board

13. OSHA requires that all material safety data sheets (MSDS) provide:
[p. 292]
a. Fire and explosion data
b. Hazard ingredient statement
c. Spill and leak control procedures
d. Standard language and terminology

14. Inherent safety of a direct-reading instrument pertains to the ability of the device to:
[p. 294]
a. Operate in hazardous atmospheres
b. Select slight changes in product concentrations
c. Monitor for both very low and very high concentrations
d. Determine the exact contaminate present

15. Which of the following devices monitors the accumulated radiation dose received by an individual:
[p. 299]
a. Radiation pagers
b. Radiation meters
c. Dosimeters
d. Passive sensors

16. Which of the following devices must be calibrated prior to use to compensate for altitude and barometric pressure:
[p. 299]
   a. pH meters
   b. Oxygen monitors
   c. Ion chambers
   d. Colorimetric indicator tubes

17. Response curves are required to read:
[p. 300]
   a. Combustible gas indicators (CGIs)
   b. Flame ionization detectors
   c. Toxic gas sensors
   d. Fourier-transform infrared spectrometry (FT-IR)

18. Which of the following devices can be susceptible to false readings if hand carried or moved around:
[p. 305]
   a. Chemical test strips
   b. Mercury detectors
   c. Photo-ionization detectors (PID)
   d. Geiger Mueller tubes

19. Which of the following monitoring instrument technology is used to monitor for explosives:
[p. 308]
   a. Flame specto-photometry
   b. Surface acoustic wave
   c. Polymerase chain reaction technology
   d. Ion-mobility spectometry

20. Which of the following is given monitoring priority if there is any doubt that the hazard is present:
[p. 311]
   a. Radiation
   b. Flammability
   c. Oxygen-deficient/enriched atmosphere
   d. Toxicity

21. If the incident involves a confined space scenario, OSHA clearly outlines the first monitoring priority as:
[p. 312]
   a. Radiation
   b. Flammability
   c. Oxygen-deficient/enriched atmosphere
   d. Toxicity

22. The following guidelines for collecting evidence samples are all true, except one:
[p. 314]
   a. Sampling tools and gloves must only be used one time for each sample
   b. Samples collected for product identification may be used for evidentiary purposes
   c. Control blanks should be provided as part of the sampling process

d. Sample containers that are certified as "clean" will have a letter stating that they are cleaned to some specification

23. What is the last stage in the Hazardous Materials Emergency Model:
[p. 318]
a. Breached
b. Engulfed
c. Over-stressed
d. Stabilized

24. There are six events in General Hazardous Materials Behavior Model (GHBMO) - stress, breach, release, engulf, impinge, and:
[p. 320]
a. Harm
b. Spill
c. Force
d. Escalate

25. True or False: Chemical stress, mechanical stress, and thermal stress can occur in combination with each other.
[p. 321]

26. Which of the following types of breach behaviors is commonly associated with catastrophic BLEVE scenarios:
[p. 322]
a. Disintegration
b. Failure of container attachments
c. Runaway cracking
d. Container punctures

27. Which of the following types of release usually offer responders adequate time to develop prolonged countermeasures:
[p. 323]
a. Detonation
b. Violent rupture
c. Rapid relief
d. Spills or leaks

28. Impingements are categorized based on:
[p. 328]
a. Duration
b. Dispersion patterns
c. Rate of release
d. The type of container

29. Etiologic harm results from:
[p. 329]
a. Exposure to poisons
b. Exposure to simple asphyxiants
c. Exposure to corrosive materials
d. Exposure to biological materials

30. The relative ability of a metal to bend or stretch without cracking is called:
[p. 332]
a. Deformation
b. Ductility
c. Density
d. Deflection

31. True or False: Tank car dent gauges cannot be used for assessing dents on cargo tank trucks due to differences in shell metal and thickness.
[p. 335]

32. True or False: The potential for ignition within a sewer collection system will be greatest at points where flammable liquids may enter or where entry is possible. (p. 341)

ANSWER KEY

Check your answers. If you missed more than six, you should read the chapter once again.

1. The temperature of a material within its container is called the:
[p. 274]
a. Ambient temperature
b. Normal physical state
c. Temperature of product
d. Critical temperature

2. Which of the following properties is the most significant for evaluating spill control options and clean-up procedures for waterborne releases:
[p. 274]
a. Specific gravity
b. Boiling point
c. Vapor pressure
d. Concentration

3. Critical temperature and critical pressure are both terms that relate to:
[p. 276]
a. The distance that gases and vapors will travel
b. The process of liquefying gases
c. The evaluation of flammability hazards of a material
d. The point at which the vapor pressure of a liquid equals atmospheric pressure

4. Miscibility is the ability of materials to:
[p. 277]
a. Float on water
b. Absorb into a permeable solid
c. Dissolve into a uniform mixture
d. Change chemically into another substance

5. Which of the following is most significant in determining the temperature at which the vapors from a flammable liquid are readily available and may ignite:
[p. 277]
a. Flash point

b. Fire point
c. Maximum safe storage temperature (MSST)
d. Self-accelerating decomposition temperature (SADT)

6. The percentage of an acid or based dissolved in water is called the:
[p. 279]
a. Strength
b. pH
c. Water reactivity
d. Concentration

7. Another term for caustic is:
[p. 279]
a. Air reactive
b. Corrosive
c. Acid
d. Base

8. The time it takes for the activity of a radioactive material to decrease to one half of its initial value through radioactive decay is called the:
[p. 280]
a. Dose
b. Dose rate
c. Half-dose
d. Half-life

9. Chemical warfare agents such as tabun, sarin, soman, and VX are all examples of:
[p. 280]
a. Nerve agents
b. Choking agents
c. Vesicants (blister agents)
d. Pathogens

10. Which of the following terms refers to the length of time a chemical agent remains as a liquid:
[p. 280]
a. Strength
b. Activity
c. Persistence
d. Oxidation ability

11. All of the guidebooks and manuals listed in Figure 7.4 are written for a target audience of:
[p. 283-286]
a. First Responders—Awareness and Operations levels
b. Hazardous Materials Technicians and Specialists
c. Incident Commanders
d. Product Specialists

12. Which of the following agencies is the federal government's central reporting point for all oil, chemical, radiological, biological, and etiological releases into the environment within the US and its territories:
    [p. 288]
    a. EPA Chemical Emergency Preparedness and Prevention Office (CEPPO)
    b. Department of Transportation National Response Center (NRC)
    c. Federal Emergency Management Agency (FEMA)
    d. U.S. Chemical Safety and Hazard Investigation Board

13. OSHA requires that all material safety data sheets (MSDS) provide:
    [p. 292]
    a. Fire and explosion data
    b. Hazard ingredient statement
    c. Spill and leak control procedures
    d. Standard language and terminology

14. Inherent safety of a direct-reading instrument pertains to the ability of the device to:
    [p. 294]
    a. Operate in hazardous atmospheres
    b. Select slight changes in product concentrations
    c. Monitor for both very low and very high concentrations
    d. Determine the exact contaminate present

15. Which of the following devices monitors the accumulated radiation dose received by an individual:
    [p. 299]
    a. Radiation pagers
    b. Radiation meters
    c. Dosimeters
    d. Passive sensors

16. Which of the following devices must be calibrated prior to use to compensate for altitude and barometric pressure:
    [p. 299]
    a. pH meters
    b. Oxygen monitors
    c. Ion chambers
    d. Colorimetric indicator tubes

17. Response curves are required to read:
    [p. 300]
    a. Combustible gas indicators (CGIs)
    b. Flame ionization detectors
    c. Toxic gas sensors
    d. Fourier-transform infrared spectrometry (FT-IR)

18. Which of the following devices can be susceptible to false readings if hand carried or moved around:
    [p. 305]
    a. Chemical test strips

b. Mercury detectors
c. Photo-ionization detectors (PID)
d. Geiger Mueller tubes

19. Which of the following monitoring instrument technology is used to monitor for explosives: [p. 308]
   a. Flame specto-photometry
   b. Surface acoustic wave
   c. Polymerase chain reaction technology
   d. Ion-mobility spectometry

20. Which of the following is given monitoring priority if there is any doubt that the hazard is present:
   [p. 311]
   a. Radiation
   b. Flammability
   c. Oxygen-deficient/enriched atmosphere
   d. Toxicity

21. If the incident involves a confined space scenario, OSHA clearly outlines the first monitoring priority as:
   [p. 312]
   a. Radiation
   b. Flammability
   c. Oxygen-deficient/enriched atmosphere
   d. Toxicity

22. The following guidelines for collecting evidence samples are all true, except one:
   [p. 314]
   a. Sampling tools and gloves must only be used one time for each sample
   b. Samples collected for product identification may be used for evidentiary purposes
   c. Control blanks should be provided as part of the sampling process
   d. Sample containers that are certified as "clean" will have a letter stating that they are cleaned to some specification

23. What is the last stage in the Hazardous Materials Emergency Model:
   [p. 318]
   a. Breached
   b. Engulfed
   c. Over-stressed
   d. Stabilized

24. There are six events in General Hazardous Materials Behavior Model (GHBMO) - stress, breach, release, engulf, impinge, and:
   [p. 320]
   a. Harm
   b. Spill
   c. Force
   d. Escalate

25. **True** or False: Chemical stress, mechanical stress, and thermal stress can occur in combination with each other.
[p. 321]

26. Which of the following types of breach behaviors is commonly associated with catastrophic BLEVE scenarios:
[p. 322]
a. Disintegration
b. Failure of container attachments
c. Runaway cracking
d. Container punctures

27. Which of the following types of release usually offer responders adequate time to develop prolonged countermeasures:
[p. 323]
a. Detonation
b. Violent rupture
c. Rapid relief
d. Spills or leaks

28. Impingements are categorized based on:
[p. 328]
a. Duration
b. Dispersion patterns
c. Rate of release
d. The type of container

29. Etiologic harm results from:
[p. 329]
a. Exposure to poisons
b. Exposure to simple asphyxiants
c. Exposure to corrosive materials
d. Exposure to biological materials

30. The relative ability of a metal to bend or stretch without cracking is called:
[p. 332]
a. Deformation
b. Ductility
c. Density
d. Deflection

31. **True** or False: Tank car dent gauges cannot be used for assessing dents on cargo tank trucks due to differences in shell metal and thickness.
[p. 335]

32. **True** or False: The potential for ignition within a sewer collection system will be greatest at points where flammable liquids may enter or where entry is possible. (p. 341)

PRACTICE

1. Visit the CHEMTREC Web site (http://www.chemtrec.org). To become more familiar with its services, use the website to answer following questions:

   a) What does the acronym CHEMTREC stand for?

   b) What are some of the 24/7 information resources that CHEMTREC has to assist callers with an incident?

   c) What types of information will the CHEMTREC emergency service specialists request when you call them for assistance?

   d) Will CHEMTREC notify other federal, state or local authorities for you in case of a haz-mat spill?

   e) Does CHEMTREC assist with handling a medical exposure?

2. Assume that you have been tasked with developing a listing of product and container specialists for terrorism and WMD agents. How will you proceed?

3. Starting with the information provided on pages 313-315, and using outside resources, including the Internet, develop a proposal to equip your department with a state-of-the art sampling equipment kit. You do not need to research costs, but you should be able to substantiate the need for the equipment or services you are proposing to acquire.

4. Using the DOT Emergency Response Guidebook (ERG) (print or online version) or other resources, estimate the area potentially impacted by a release of the following hazmats. Assume you have a large release, such as a one-ton cylinder, a tank truck or a railcar.

Sulfur Mustard	Fire Isolation:	
	Spill Isolation: (meters)	Downwind: (miles)
Phosgene	Fire Isolation:	
	Isolation: (meters)	Downwind: (miles)
Sarin	Fire Isolation:	
	Spill Isolation: (meters)	Downwind: (miles)
Chlorine	Fire Isolation:	
	Isolation: (meters)	Downwind: (miles)

5. Go to http://www.8stepprocess.com for additional information and activities pertaining to Chapter 7 "Hazard Assessment and Risk Evaluation."

IMPORTANT TERMINOLOGY

The following are all general chemical terms that you should know. Review the definitions of these terms and the others found on pages 273 and 274. Then practice your recall of the terms by playing the unscramble game, below:

- Element
- Compound
- Mixture
- Solution
- Slurry
- Hydrocarbons

1. Xretuim ____________

   Substance made up of two or more elements or compounds, physically mixed together.

2. Rusylr ______________

   Pourable mixture of a solid and a liquid.

3. Oyrandobschr ______________

Compounds primarily made up of hydrogen and carbon.

4. Eneetlm ____________

Pure substance that cannot be broken down into simpler substances by chemical means.

5. Numoopcd ____________

Chemical combination of two or more elements, either the same elements or different ones, that is electrically neutral.

6. Tunoliso ____________

Mixture in which all of the ingredients are completely dissolved.

Matching: On the line next to each term in Column A, print the letter of its definition from Column B.

Column A Terms	**Column B Definitions**
7.______Ionic bonding (p. 273)	A. Compounds derived from other than vegetable or animal sources which lack carbon chains but may contain a carbon atom (e.g., sulfur dioxide—SO_2).
8.______Covalent bonding (p. 273)	B. A hydrocarbon containing the benzene "ring," which is formed by six carbon atoms and contains resonant bonds. Examples include benzene (C_6H_6) and toluene (C_7H_8).
9.______Organic materials (p. 273)	C. A hydrocarbon possessing only single covalent bonds, and all of the carbon atoms are saturated with hydrogen. May also be referred to as alkanes. Examples include methane (CH_4), propane (C_3H_8), and butane (C_4H_{10}).
10.______Inorganic materials (p. 273)	D. A hydrocarbon with at least one multiple bond between two carbon atoms somewhere in the molecule. May also be referred to as the alkenes and alkynes.
11.______Saturated hydrocarbons (p. 273-274)	E. The force holding together atoms that share electrons.
12.______Unsaturated hydrocarbons (p. 274)	F. The electrostatic attraction of oppositely charged particles.
13.______Aromatic hydrocarbons (p. 274)	G. A hydrocarbon with halogen atom (e.g., chlorine, fluorine, bromine, etc.) substituted for a hydrogen

atom. They are often more toxic than naturally occurring organic chemicals, and they decompose into smaller, more harmful elements when exposed to high temperatures for a sustained period of time.

14.______Halogenated hydrocarbons (p. 274)

H. Materials that contain two or more carbon atoms; derived from materials that are living or were once living, such as plants or decayed products. Most are flammable.

On the line next to each physical property in Column A, print the letter of its definition from Column B.

Column A **Physical Property**	**Column B** **Definitions**
15.______Vapor density (p. 275)	A. The temperature at which a liquid changes its phase to a vapor or gas.
16.______Boiling point (p. 275)	B. The weight of a pure vapor or gas compared with the weight of an equal volume of dry air at the same temperature and pressure.
17.______Melting point (p. 275)	C. The weight of a solid or liquid material as compared with the weight of an equal volume of water.
18.______Sublimation (p. 276)	D. The ease with which a liquid or solid can pass into the vapor state.
19.______Volatility (p. 276)	E. The ability of a substance to change from the solid to the vapor phase without passing through the liquid phase
20.______Viscosity (p. 277)	F. The temperature at which a solid changes its phase to a liquid. (This temperature is also the freezing point depending on the direction of the change.)
	G. Measurement of the thickness of a liquid and its ability to flow.

ANSWER KEY

1. Mixture–Substance made up of two or more elements or compounds, physically mixed together.
2. Slurry– Pourable mixture of a solid and a liquid.
3. Hydrocarbons–Compounds primarily made up of hydrogen and carbon.
4. Element–Pure substance that cannot be broken down into simpler substances by chemical means.
5. Compound–Chemical combination of two or more elements, either the same elements or different ones, that is electrically neutral.
6. Solution–Mixture in which all of the ingredients are completely dissolved.

Matching:

Column A **Terms**	**Column B** **Definitions**
7.__F__Ionic bonding (p. 273)	A. Compounds derived from other than vegetable or animal sources which lack carbon chains but may contain a carbon atom (e.g., sulfur dioxide—SO_2).
8.__E__Covalent bonding (p. 273)	B. A hydrocarbon containing the benzene "ring," which is formed by six carbon atoms and contains resonant bonds. Examples include benzene (C_6H_6) and toluene (C_7H_8).
9.__H__Organic materials (p. 273)	C. A hydrocarbon possessing only single covalent bonds, and all of the carbon atoms are saturated with hydrogen. May also be referred to as alkanes. Examples include methane (CH_4), propane (C_3H_8), and butane (C_4H_{10}).
10.__A__Inorganic materials	D. A hydrocarbon with at least one multiple bond between two carbon atoms somewhere in the mole cule. May also be referred to as the alkenes and alkynes.
11.__C__Saturated hydrocarbons (p. 273-274)	E. The force holding together atoms that share electrons.
12.__D__Unsaturated hydrocarbons (p. 274)	F. The electrostatic attraction of oppositely charged particles.
13.__B__Aromatic hydrocarbons (p. 274)	G. A hydrocarbon with halogen atom (e.g., chlorine, fluorine, bromine, etc.) substituted for a hydrogen atom. They are often more toxic than naturally occurring organic chemicals, and they decompose into smaller, more harmful elements when exposed to high temperatures for a sustained period of time.
14.__G__Halogenated hydrocarbons (p. 274)	H. Materials that contain two or more carbon atoms; derived from materials that are living or were once living, such as plants or decayed products. Most are flammable.

On the line next to each physical property in Column A, print the letter of its definition from Column B.

Column A **Physical Property**	**Column B** **Definitions**
15.__B__Vapor density (p. 275)	A. The temperature at which a liquid changes its phase to a vapor or gas.
16.__A__Boiling point (p. 275)	B. The weight of a pure vapor or gas compared with the weight of an equal volume of dry air at the same temperature and pressure.

17.___F___Melting point (p. 275)	C. The weight of a solid or liquid material as compared with the weight of an equal volume of water.
18.___E___Sublimation (p. 276)	D. The ease with which a liquid or solid can pass into the vapor state.
19.___D___Volatility (p. 276)	E. The ability of a substance to change from the solid to the vapor phase without passing through the liquid phase
20.___G___Viscosity (p. 277)	F. The temperature at which a solid changes its phase to a liquid. (This temperature is also the freezing point depending on the direction of the change.)
	G. Measurement of the thickness of a liquid and its ability to flow.

STUDY GROUP ACTIVITY

1. On page 281 of the text, the authors state that "too much information can sometimes be as bad as too little information." As a group, discuss and exchange ideas and solutions for managing and prioritizing information needs.

2. Ludwig Benner is a pioneer in the field of hazardous materials. He developed both the DECIDE process for analyzing an incident and the General Hazardous Materials Behavior Model (GEBMO) for hazardous materials. He has recorded in an essay his personal experiences investigating hazmat emergencies that led to the development of both these models. This "Story of GEBMO" is archived with other personal papers at http://members.cox.net/lbjr05/. Individually, group members should read this essay carefully and then discuss their thoughts on the paper as a group.

3. Assume you have an incident involving a release of gasoline into a sewer collection system. Half of the group should prepare a presentation on how to determine if the source of the problem is a spill/dumping directly into the sewer collection system; the other half of the group should prepare a presentation on how to determine if the source of the problem is a subsurface release, such as a breached underground storage tank or pipeline. Both groups then make and discuss their presentations.

STUDY GROUP LEARNING THROUGH INQUIRY SCENARIO 7-1

You are the Incident Commander on the scene of a overturned 7,000 gallon MC-307/DOT-407 cargo tank truck carrying toluene. The vehicle is located at an interchange of two major highways. The tank is leaking at a large rate from the manway area, and a large volume of product has pooled in and around the vehicle.

Based on this limited information answer the following questions using the material from Chapter 7:

1) What hazards are present? (Review pages 217 to 272, Chapter 7.)

2) What types of monitoring instruments should be used? Be specific! (Review pages 297 to 305, Chapter 7.) Why would you use the instrument that you selected over another type that is available. What other air monitoring instruments could you use to confirm the presence and concentrations of toluene?

3) Nearby businesses are complaining about strong odors in the area and in their buildings. The TLV/TWA for toluene is 100 ppm and the IDLH value is 2,000 ppm. Using the combustible gas indicator available within your organization, First Responders are getting readings of 5% of the lower explosive limit (LEL) outside of these structures. The CGI is calibrated on pentane and the conversion factor is 1.2, with a 25% margin of error. Is there a hazard to unprotected individuals within the area where the reading was obtained? How would you proceed? (Review figure 2.7, page 55, Chapter 2.)

4) What risks are involved in this incident? How would you justify taking or not taking the risks you described based on the hazards present? How would you describe these risks to the businesses who are complaining about the strong odors of toluene?

STUDY GROUP LEARNING THROUGH INQUIRY SCENARIO 7-2

You are the Incident Commander and arrive on the scene of a confined spaces incident involving a man trapped inside of a vertical storage tank which is 27 feet high and approximately 18 feet in diameter. The only manway on the tank is 36 inches in diameter and is on the top of the tank. The facility manager informs you that the tank was being repaired by an outside contractor. The tank is empty and was cleaned prior to entry, but previously contained ethylene dibromide (EDB). You send a fully protected HMRT member to the top of the tank to look inside. She reports back to you that the victim is motionless, in a seated position, and has an SCBA unit on with the facepiece in place. You confirm that the contractor has been inside the tank approximately 10 minutes.

Using the background information provided and the information discussed in Chapter 7 answer the following questions:

1) Would you attempt a confined spaces rescue based on the information you have been provided? If so, what precautions would you take based on what you have learned in Chapter 7? (Also review pages 55 to 57, Chapter 2.)

2) Would you attempt a rescue if the contractor had been in the tank for 15 minutes? If you answered yes, what do you base this decision on? If you answered no, would you attempt a rescue if the person trapped inside the tank was an off-duty firefighter and you knew him personally? What if the person were a member of your family, would this influence your decision? (Review pages 432 to 434, Chapter 10.)

3) Would you attempt a rescue if the contractor had been in the tank for 25 minutes? What if a member of your Emergency Response Team personally knew the contractor, would this change your answer?

SUMMARY AND REVIEW

1. Risk levels are variable and change from incident to incident. Factors that influence the level of risk include the hazardous nature of the material(s) involved and the quantity of the material. Identify at least two other variables that influence the level of risk:

2. Given the fact that anhydrous ammonia has a molecular weight of 17, how do we know that it will rise if released?

3. Given the follow evaporation rates of the following materials, which one will evaporate the slowest:

   a. Mineral spirits = 0.1
   b. Xylene = 0.6
   c. Methy ethyl ketone = 3.8
   d. Acetone = 5.6

4. Which of the following statements about vapor pressure is true:

   a. The vapor pressure of a substance at 100°F is always higher than the vapor pressure at 68°F
   b. Vapor pressures reported in millimeters of mercury (mm Hg) are usually very low pressures
   c. The lower the boiling point of a liquid, the greater vapor pressure at a given temperature
   d. All of the above

5. What is the relationship between expansion ratio and the amount of gas produced by evaporation:

6. Which of the following is a significant property in evaluating the selection of control and extinguishing agents, including the use of water and firefighting foams:
   a. Relative gas density
   b. Boiling point
   c. Solubility
   d. Viscosity

7. What happens to the flammable range if a gas or vapor is released into an oxygen-enriched atmosphere:

8. Toxic byproducts of the combustion process are based on the burning material(s). If nitrogen is present, incomplete combustion can produce:

9. Reactive materials include materials that decompose spontaneously, polymerize, or otherwise self-react, such as oxidizers. Identify at least one other reactive material:

10. Assume you are the incident commander at a hazmat release and you need to initiate a conference phone call between your on-scene responders and company representatives. You also need to have MSDSs faxed to you. What organization can do this for you?

11. Identify at least two criteria that should be used when evaluating electronic-based information sources:

12. What is "instrument response time?"

13. If air monitoring provides no information on the identity or hazard class of the unknown material, what should the next step be?

14. What method can be used to help responders avoid being overwhelmed by the volume of hazard information collected during the course of an incident?

15. Examine the Hazardous Materials Emergency Model on page 318. At what stages are emergency response countermeasures applied to influence the progression of events:

16. The following chart is based on the General Hazardous Materials Behavior Model. Some of the event categories have been filled in. Fill in at least one additional blank for each event:

EVENT					
Stress:	**Breach:**	**Release:**	**Engulf:**	**Impinge:**	**Harm:**
Thermal	Disintegration	Detonation	Cloud	Short term	Thermal
Radiation	Punctures	Leak	Cone	Medium term	Etiologic

17. Assume you have an incident involving a pressurized bulk transportation container. What should you do if you are unsure of the container or how the container is likely to breach?

18. The movement of hazardous materials through soil will be dependent on the viscosity of the liquid. Identify two other variables that influence the movement:

19. Although combustible gas indicators (CGIs) are excellent tools for evaluating flammable atmospheres, they may not be very effective for assessing low-level flammable concentrations such as found with subsurface and sewer spills. Why? Which instruments are better suited for these scenarios?

20. The probability of an explosion within an underground space will depend on two factors: 1) that a flammable atmosphere exists, and 2):

SUMMARY AND REVIEW ANSWER KEY

1. To be correct, your answer should include at least two of the following:
   - Containment system and type of stress applied to the container.
   - Proximity of exposures.
   - Level of available resources (p. 217)

2. The molecular weight of air is 29; materials with a molecular weight of <29 will rise, and those with a molecular weight >29 will sink. (p. 275)

3. a. Mineral spirits = 0.1 (p. 276)

4. d. All of the above (p. 276)

5. The greater the expansion ratio, the more gas that is produced and the larger the hazard area. (p. 276)

6. c. Solubility (p. 277)

7. If a gas or vapor is released into an oxygen-enriched atmosphere, the flammable range will expand. (p. 278)

8. Hydrogen cyanide and ammonia (p. 278)

9. To be correct, your answer must include at least one of the following:

   Organic peroxides, corrosives, pyrophoric materials, water reactive materials. (p. 278)

10. CHEMTREC (p. 287)

11. To be correct, your answer must include at least one of the following:
    - How will the tool complement or improve your response operations and decision making?

- Costs, including initial subscription and user fees
- Hardware and software requirements, including communications technology
- Communications security (COMSEC), as appropriate
- Ease of use and user friendliness
- Technical support (p. 290)

12. Also known as lag time, this is the period of time between when the instrument senses a product and when a monitor reading is produced. (p. 293)

13. If air monitoring provides no information on the identity or hazard class of the unknown, responders may collect a sample to conduct field tests of the material, or send the sample to a lab for further analysis. (p.313)

14. Many responders rely on printed data forms and checklists to ensure that all information requirements have been prioritized and addressed. (p. 317)

15. Stage 4: Escalate, Stage 7: Initial Injury, and Stage 8: Subsiding (p. 318)

16. The following chart is based on the General Hazardous Materials Behavior Model. Some of the event categories have been filled in. Fill in at least one additional black for each event:

EVENT					
Stress:	**Breach:**	**Release:**	**Engulf:**	**Impinge:**	**Harm:**
Thermal	Disintegration	Detonation	Cloud	Short term	Thermal
Radiation	Punctures	Leak	Cone	Medium term	Etiologic
Chemical	Runaway cracking	Spill	Plume	Long term	Mechanical
Mechanical	Attachments opening	Violent rupture	Stream		Radiation
	Splits or tears	Rapid Relief	Irregular Deposit		Asphyxiation
					Corrosivity
					Toxicity / poisons

17. Get assistance from product or container specialists. This may include railroad personnel, gas industry representatives, and cargo tank truck specialists. (p. 335)

18. Properties of the soil and the rate of release (p. 338)

19. To register a positive reading, many CGIs require a concentration of up to 10,000 ppm (1% in air). While this may not be a flammable concentration, it often represents a significant environmental problem. Photoionization detectors (PIDs) are better suited for these scenarios. (p. 338)

20. 2) that an ignition source is present. (p. 339)

SELF EVALUATION

Please review all your work in this lesson. Now that you have completed this lesson, please take about 15 minutes to note your stronger and weaker areas.

Overall I feel I did (very well / well / fair / not so well) on the acronyms and abbreviations exercise.

Overall I feel I did (very well / well / fair / not so well) on the self-test questions.

Overall I feel did (very well / well / fair / not so well) on the terminology exercise.

Overall I feel I did (very well / well / fair / not so well) on the summary and review questions.

When compared to the previous lessons, I think I performed (better / worse / equally well).

List two areas in Chapter 7 in which you feel you could improve your skill or knowledge level:

1.

2.

Consider the following self-evaluation questions as they pertain to Chapter 7:

Am I taking effective margin notes?

Am I dedicating enough quality time to my studies?

Is anything distracting my focus?

Was any part of Chapter 7 too advanced for me?

Did I find that I don't have enough background experience to sufficiently grasp certain subject areas?

For areas in which I did particularly well, was it because I'm particularly interested in that subject matter? How so?

Were some things easier to learn because I have prior experience in learning or working with the concepts or principles?

Did I find that certain portions of the textbook seem to be better organized and effective in explaining key points?

What other Students have had to say about Chapter 7 material:

"Some of the information like General Hazardous Materials Behavior Model is detail intensive and takes some time to look over and learn.

The topic of the General Hazardous Materials Behavior Model was a new concept to me. I think it is a great tool to better understand the dynamics of a hazardous materials incident.

It's very important that I understand and be able to establish goals, objectives and tactical plans. The next most important but linked to the first is understanding the General Hazardous Materials Behavior model. Knowing that will help keep me safe and accomplish the first.

Working the variables of atmospheric conditions when trying to determine what a cloud will do has never been my favorite part of hazmat response. Simply being conservative and overestimating the potential hazard a cloud or plume will offer always leaves me feeling uneasy. Fortunately, I have never underestimated the potential for harm but I have seen careers ruined by those that have.

As a lieutenant in charge of the engine company I feel that it is important that I master most, if not all, of the objectives of this chapter. A key to assuring the safety of my crew and myself is to be able to properly analyze the hazards and risks associated with the incident.

In my role as captain, there are many instances where I am the first officer on scene. It is critical for me to master the practice the hazard and risk analysis. Before any operations begin, a thorough hazard and risk analysis needs to be performed to better understand what is happening and to determine the most appropriate course of action."

Pat on the Back

Congratulations on working though Chapter 7 in the textbook and for completing the exercises in this lesson.

CHAPTER 8

SELECT PERSONAL PROTECTIVE CLOTHING AND EQUIPMENT

CHAPTER ORIENTATION

Open the text to page 350. Take about 10 minutes to skim the chapter. Pay attention to the boldface subject headings. Read the titles to all the figures and note how they fit into the subject headings. Scan the case studies. Please read the introduction and summary sections carefully. When you have finished looking through Chapter 8, respond to the following items. Please use the textbook as you jot down your comments in the spaces provided below:

1. Were you surprised to learn that there were no NFPA standards for chemical protective clothing at the time of the Benicia (California) chemical suit incident in 1983? Have you ever considered what it would be like today if standards, such as NFPA 1991–Vapor Protective Ensembles for Hazardous Materials Emergencies, had not be written? (See page 352 in the text.)

2. Reflect on your current level of knowledge or background experience about the topics covered in Chapter 8. Where have you read about, learned about, or applied this knowledge in the past?

3. What sections or parts of Chapter 8 strike you as looking especially interesting?

4. What particular subjects in this chapter are important for a person in your position to master?

5. What do you predict will be the hardest things for you to learn in this chapter?

LEARNING OBJECTIVES

Turn to page 350-351 and examine the chapter objectives. When you have finished, respond to the following question:

1. Which objectives in Chapter 8 do you feel you can achieve right now, with a reasonable level of confidence?

Highlight or place a check mark next to those objectives on pages 350-351 that addresses educational competencies referenced in *NFPA 472—Professional Competence of Responders to Hazardous Materials*.

As you read the sections of the chapter that deal with the objectives you have identified above, make sure your ideas or knowledge base match those of the authors. If not, you should examine how your current understanding of the material differs from that of the authors'. Depending on the level at which you wish to master the subject, discrepancies will have to be rectified and gaps will need to be filled.

ABBREVIATIONS AND ACRONYMS

The following abbreviations and acronyms are used in Chapter 8:

APR	Air Purifying Respirator (p. 365, 367)
ARFF	Aircraft Rescue Firefighting (p. 380, 381)

ASTM	American Society of Testing and Materials (355, 360, 363)
CPC	Chemical Protective Clothing (p. 352, 353, 354, 355, 356, 357, 358, 361, 363, 370, 373, 374, 375, 376, 379, 382, 386, 387)
ESLI	End-of-Service-Life Indicator (p. 366)
HAZMAT	Hazardous Materials (p. 352, 353, 358, 364, 365, 367, 370, 372, 373, 374, 375, 379, 380, 381, 382, 383, 384, 385, 386, 387, 389)
HMRT	Hazardous Materials Response Team (p. 379, 381, 385, 386)
MDPR	Minimum Detectable Permeation Rate (p. 356)
NIOSH	National Institute for Occupational Safety and Health (p. 364, 365, 367, 368, 369)
PAPR	Powered Air-Purifying Respirator (p. 361, 362, 363, 365, 366, 367, 374)
PNA	Polynuclear Aromatic Compounds (p. 371)
PPE	Personal Protective Clothing and Equipment (351, 352, 354, 370, 382, 386, 387, 388, 389)
PVA	Polyvinyl Alcohol (p. 372)
PVC	Polyvinyl Chloride (p. 359, 364, 375, 378)
RDECOM	U.S. Army Research, Development, and Engineering Command (p. 373)
SAR	Supplied Air Respirator (p. 367, 368, 374, 384)
SCBA	Self-Contained Breathing Apparatus (p. 361, 367, 368, 370, 371, 372, 373, 374, 375, 376, 377, 378, 379, 380, 381, 382, 383, 384, 387)
SDL	System Detection Limit (p. 356)
SEI	Safety Equipment Institute (p. 360)
SFC	Structural Firefighting Clothing (p. 370, 371, 372, 373)
UL	Underwriters Laboratories (p. 360)

Locate these abbreviations and acronyms in the textbook (page numbers provided above) and underline them. Read the paragraph in which they are used.

Fill in the blank using the abbreviations and acronyms above.

1. Gloves made of this material have excellent compatibility against certain petroleum solvents but break down on exposure to water: __________

2. These devices remove particulate matter, gases or vapors from the atmosphere: __________

3. The minimum amount of chemical breakthrough that can be detected by the laboratory analytical system being used for the permeation test: __________

4. Equipment provided to shield or isolate a person from the chemical, physical, and thermal hazards that may be encountered at a hazardous materials incident: __________

ABBREVIATIONS AND ACRONYMS CROSSWORD

Use the clues below to solve the crossword.

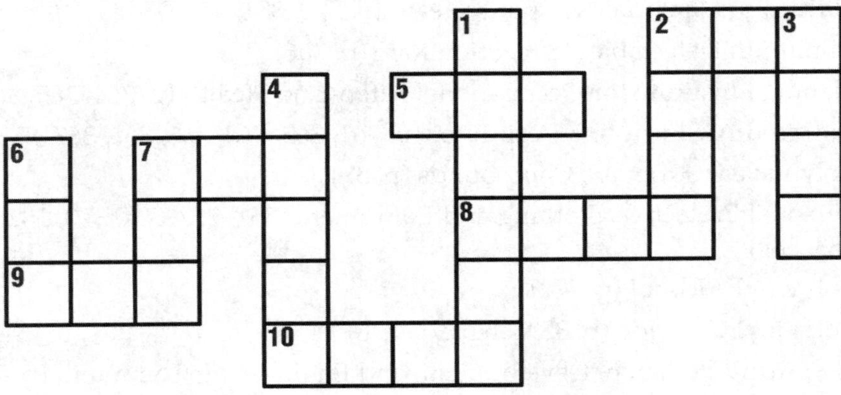

Across

2. This product of combustion has led to increased concerns with the contamination and decontamination of structural firefighting clothing

5. Positive pressure respirator that is supplied by either an airline hose or breathing air cylinders connected to the respirator by a short airline.

7. This organization certifies chemical protective clothing performance

8. The minimum permeation rate that can be detected by the laboratory analytical system being used for the permeation test.

9. These single or multi-piece garments are specially designed and configured to protect the wearer's torso, head, arms, legs, hands, etc.

10. This organized group of employees is expected to perform work to handle and control actual or potential leaks or spills of hazardous substances requiring possible close approach to the substance.

Down

1. This material jumps out of its container when something goes wrong and harms the things it touches

2. Air purifying respirators that use a blower to force the ambient air through air-purifying elements to a fullface mask.

3. Proximity suits are often needed for conducting these operations.

4. A Federal agency that tests and certifies respiratory protective devices.

6. Reusable garment materials are usually made from this material

7. Protective clothing normally worn by firefighters during structural fire fighting operations.

ANSWER KEY

1. Gloves made of this material have excellent compatibility against certain petroleum solvents but break down on exposure to water: PVA

2. These devices remove particulate matter, gases or vapors from the atmosphere: APR

3. The minimum amount of chemical breakthrough that can be detected by the laboratory analytical system being used for the permeation test: SDL

4. Equipment provided to shield or isolate a person from the chemical, physical, and thermal hazards that may be encountered at a hazardous materials incident: PPE

The Crossword Answer Key is at the end of this chapter.

STUDY SESSION OVERVIEW

Read pages 350 to the top of page 370, then take a short break to think about what you have read. Then read the rest of the chapter. Take margin notes as you go. Underline or highlight phrases that you feel are important.

When you have completed your reading, respond to the following questions. You may use the textbook to help you answer the questions, or work from memory.

1. What is the operational goal of "Select Personal Protective Clothing and Equipment?" (Hint: return to Chapter 4, page 137 if you need help)

2. In your own words, explain what is meant by the statement that "PPE is NOT your first line of defense; it is your last line of defense."

3. Wearing any type and level of impermeable protective clothing creates the potential for heat stress injuries. Review the section on heat stress in Chapter 2 (page 61). What are the signs and symptoms of heat cramps, heat exhaustion, and heat stroke?

4. The selection and use of specialized protective clothing at a hazmat emergency should be approached from a systems perspective. Briefly describe this system.

5. Assume you are the Hazmat Group Safety Officer or other Hazmat Group personnel (e.g., Entry Leader). You are about to conduct a pre-entry safety briefing. What topics will you include in your briefing?

6. What kinds of information should be recorded for all chemical vapor protective clothing?

SELF-TEST

Answer the following questions. You may use the textbook to help you answer the questions, or work from memory.

Select the best term from the following list to answer questions #1-7. You may write the word or its letter (a, b, or c) in the blank. (p. 353-354)

a. Degradation
b. Penetration
c. Permeation

1. _________ is the physical destruction or decomposition of a clothing material due to exposure to chemicals, use, or ambient conditions.

2. _________ is the process by which a hazardous chemical moves through a given material on the molecular level.

3. _________ is the flow or movement of a hazardous chemical through closures, seams, porous materials, and pinholes or other imperfections in the material.

4. _________ can lead to protective clothing failures when breakthrough times are exceeded.

5. _________ can be caused by clothing material degradation, manufacturing defects, physical damage to the suit (e.g., punctures, abrasions, etc.), normal wear and tear, and PPE defects.

6. _________ resistance data are provided as "pass" or "fail" relative to the specific chemical or mixture tested.

7. _________ is noted by visible signs such as charring, shrinking, swelling, color change or dissolving, or by testing the clothing material for weight changes, stiffening, loss of fabric tensile strength, and so on.

8. The following statements about breakthrough time are all true, except one :
[p. 355]
   a. Breakthrough time is measured in units of minutes or hours
   b. Breakthrough times are determined by laboratory testing procedures
   c. Breakthrough time is defined as the time from the initial chemical attack on the outside of the material to its detection inside
   d. Breakthrough time is the only reliable measure of chemical resistance

9. Chemical permeation through protective clothing is a three step process – absorption, diffusion, and:
[p. 355]
   a. Adsorption
   b. Desorption
   c. Disintegration
   d. Evaporation

10. For reference purposes, a permeation rate of .9m/cm^2/min is equal to:
[p. 355]
   a. 1 drop per minute
   b. 1 dram per minute
   c. 1 drop per hour
   d. 1 milliliter per 12 hour period

11. True or False: Once a chemical has begun the diffusion process, it may continue to diffuse even after the chemical itself has been removed from the outside surface of the material. (p. 357)

12. True / False: Chemical protective clothing is not appropriate for firefighting operations, or for protection in flammable or explosive environments.
[p. 357]

13. The most critical factor in evaluating and choosing chemical protective clothing is:
[p. 357]
   a. Shelf life
   b. Chemical resistance
   c. Flexibility
   d. Decontamination and disposal

14. The following statements about NFPA 1994 – Protective Ensemble for Chemical/Biological Terrorism Incidents are all true, except one:
[p. 361]
a. NFPA 1994 was originally enacted in 2001 as a result of the growing terrorism problem.
b. Many of the NFPA1994 testing requirements are similar to those found in both NFPA1991 and 1992.
c. All NFPA 1994 ensembles (i.e., garment, gloves and footwear) are reusable
d. NFPA 1994 defines three classes of ensembles based on the perceived threats at an incident

15. The _____ Respirator Certification Requirements outline the requirements for particulate respirators:
[p. 365]
a. NIOSH
b. ASTM
c. EPA
d. NFPA

Place an X next to each statement to indicate whether the statement pertains only to APRs (air purification respirators), PAPRs (powered-air purification respirators), or pertains to both:

APR	PAPR	
		16. Can be found with either a full-face or half-face configuration (p. 365)
		17. Are a negative pressure respirators (p. 365)
		18. Have a protection factor of 50:1 (p. 365)
		19. Have a protection factor of 1000:1 (p. 365)
		20. Are rated according to filter efficiency degradation (p. 365)
		21. Cannot be used in IDLH environments (p. 365)
		22. Should not be used in the presence or potential presence of unidentified contaminants (p. 366)
		23. Are well-suited for operations involving solids, dusts, and powders (p. 366)

24. The following are all components of a supplied air respirator (SAR), except one:
[p. 368]
a. Airline hose
b. Source of breathing air
c. Positive-pressure respirator
d. Alkaline scrubber

25. Which of the following personal protective equipment must be worn (not optional) for EPA Level A chemical protection:
[p. 369]
a. Air-supplied respiratory protection
b. Hard hat
c. Coveralls
d. Long-john type cotton underwear

26. Which of the following EPA levels of chemical protection is the minimum level recommended on initial site entries until the hazards have been further identified and defined:
[p.369]
a. Level A
b. Level B
c. Level C
d. Level D

27. Structural firefighting clothing (SFC) is normally not the first PPE choice for most hazmat response scenarios, except when the incident involves:
[p.370]
a. Corrosives and PCBs
b. Cyanide compounds
c. Infectious bloodborne diseases
d. Flammable gas and liquid fire incidents

28. What is the minimum level of respiratory protection when wearing structural firefighting clothing in hazmat environments:
[p.372]
a. Half-face air purification respirators
b. Full face air purification respirators
c. Powered-air purification respirators
d. Positive-pressure SCBA

29. Liquid chemical splash protective clothing may be used when:
[p. 374]

__yes / __no: The vapors or gases present are not suspected of containing high concen trations of chemicals that are harmful to, or can be absorbed by, the skin.

__ yes / __no: It is highly unlikely that the user will be exposed to high concentrations of vapors, gases, or liquid chemicals that will affect any exposed skin areas.

__ yes / __no: Operations will not be conducted in a flammable atmosphere.

30. Chemical vapor protective clothing should be used when:
[p. 376]

__ yes / __no: Extremely hazardous substances are known or suspected to be present, and skin contact is possible

__ yes / __no: Anticipated operations involve unknown or unidentified substances and the scenario dictates that vapor-tight skin protection is required.

31. High-temperature protective clothing is designed primarily for ________ heat exposures: [p.380]
   a. Ambient
   b. Conductive
   c. Radiant
   d. None of the above

32. There are two types of high-temperature protective clothing – 1) proximity suits and 2): [p.381]
   a. Fire entry suits
   b. Flash overgarments
   c. Aluminized suits
   d. Insulation suits

ANSWER KEY

Check your answers. If you missed more than three, you should read the chapter once again.

a. Degradation
b. Penetration
c. Permeation

1. a. Degradation is the physical destruction or decomposition of a clothing material due to exposure to chemicals, use, or ambient conditions.

2. c. Permeation is the process by which a hazardous chemical moves through a given material on the molecular level.

3. b. Penetration is the flow or movement of a hazardous chemical through closures, seams, porous materials, and pinholes or other imperfections in the material.

4. c. Permeation can lead to protective clothing failures when breakthrough times are exceeded.

5. b. Penetration can be caused by clothing material degradation, manufacturing defects, physical damage to the suit (e.g., punctures, abrasions, etc.), normal wear and tear, and PPE defects.

6. b. Penetration resistance data are provided as "pass" or "fail" relative to the specific chemical or mixture tested.

7. a. Degradation is noted by visible signs such as charring, shrinking, swelling, color change or dissolving, or by testing the clothing material for weight changes, stiffening, loss of fabric tensile strength, and so on.

8. The following statements about breakthrough time are all true, except one : [p. 355]
   a. Breakthrough time is measured in units of minutes or hours
   b. Breakthrough times are determined by laboratory testing procedures
   c. Breakthrough time is defined as the time from the initial chemical attack on the outside of the material to its detection inside
   d. Breakthrough time is the only reliable measure of chemical resistance

9. Chemical permeation through protective clothing is a three step process – absorption, diffusion, and:
[p. 355]
   a. Adsorption
   b. Desorption
   c. Disintegration
   d. Evaporation

10. For reference purposes, a permeation rate of .9m/cm^2/min is equal to:
[p. 355]
   a. 1 drop per minute
   b. 1 dram per minute
   c. 1 drop per hour
   d. 1 milliliter per 12 hour period

11. **True** or False: Once a chemical has begun the diffusion process, it may continue to diffuse even after the chemical itself has been removed from the outside surface of the material. (p. 357)

12. **True** / False: Chemical protective clothing is not appropriate for firefighting operations, or for protection in flammable or explosive environments.
[p. 357]

13. The most critical factor in evaluating and choosing chemical protective clothing is:
[p. 357]
   a. Shelf life
   b. Chemical resistance
   c. Flexibility
   d. Decontamination and disposal

14. The following statements about NFPA 1994 – Protective Ensemble for Chemical/Biological Terrorism Incidents are all true, except one:
[p. 361]
   a. NFPA 1994 was originally enacted in 2001 as a result of the growing terrorism problem.
   b. Many of the NFPA1994 testing requirements are similar to those found in both NFPA1991 and 1992.
   c. All NFPA 1994 ensembles (i.e., garment, gloves and footwear) are reusable
   d. NFPA 1994 defines three classes of ensembles based on the perceived threats at an incident

15. The _____ Respirator Certification Requirements outline the requirements for particulate respirators:
[p. 365]
   a. NIOSH
   b. ASTM
   c. EPA
   d. NFPA

Place an X next to each statement to indicate whether the statement pertains only to APRs (air purification respirators), PAPRs (powered-air purification respirators), or pertains to both:

APR	PAPR	
X		16. Can be found with either a full-face or half-face configuration (p. 365)
X		17. Are a negative pressure respirators (p. 365)
X		18. Have a protection factor of 50:1 (p. 365)
	X	19. Have a protection factor of 1000:1 (p. 365)
X	X	20. Are rated according to filter efficiency degradation (p. 365)
X	X	21. Cannot be used in IDLH environments (p. 365)
X	X	22. Should not be used in the presence or potential presence of unidentified contaminants (p. 366)
X	X	23. Are well-suited for operations involving solids, dusts, and powders (p. 366)

24. The following are all components of a supplied air respirator (SAR), except one: [p. 368]
    a. Airline hose
    b. Source of breathing air
    c. Positive-pressure respirator
    d. Alkaline scrubber

25. Which of the following personal protective equipment must be worn (not optional) for EPA Level A chemical protection: [p. 369]
    a. Air-supplied respiratory protection
    b. Hard hat
    c. Coveralls
    d. Long-john type cotton underwear

26. Which of the following EPA levels of chemical protection is the minimum level recommended on initial site entries until the hazards have been further identified and defined: [p.369]
    a. Level A
    b. Level B
    c. Level C
    d. Level D

27. Structural firefighting clothing (SFC) is normally not the first PPE choice for most hazmat response scenarios, except when the incident involves:
[p.370]
a. Corrosives and PCBs
b. Cyanide compounds
c. Infectious bloodborne diseases
d. Flammable gas and liquid fire incidents

28. What is the minimum level of respiratory protection when wearing structural firefighting clothing in hazmat environments:
[p.372]
a. Half-face air purification respirators
b. Full face air purification respirators
c. Powered-air purification respirators
d. Positive-pressure SCBA

29. Liquid chemical splash protective clothing may be used when:
[p. 374]

yes / __no: The vapors or gases present are not suspected of containing high con centrations of chemicals that are harmful to, or can be absorbed by, the skin.

yes / __no: It is highly unlikely that the user will be exposed to high concentrations of vapors, gases, or liquid chemicals that will affect any exposed skin areas.

yes / __no: Operations will not be conducted in a flammable atmosphere.

30. Chemical vapor protective clothing should be used when:
[p. 376]

yes / __no: Extremely hazardous substances are known or suspected to be present, and skin contact is possible

yes / __no: Anticipated operations involve unknown or unidentified substances and the scenario dictates that vapor-tight skin protection is required.

31. High-temperature protective clothing is designed primarily for ________ heat exposures:
[p.380]
a. Ambient
b. Conductive
c. Radiant
d. None of the above

32. There are two types of high-temperature protective clothing – 1) proximity suits and 2):
[p.381]
a. Fire entry suits
b. Flash overgarments
c. Aluminized suits
d. Insulation suits

PRACTICE

1. Develop procedures to address one or more of the following scenarios involving chemical vapor suits:
   - Loss of air supply
   - Loss of suit integrity
   - Loss of communications
   - Buddy down in the hot zone

2. Go to http://www.8stepprocess.com for additional information and activities pertaining to Chapter 8 "Select Personal Protective Clothing and Equipment."

STUDY GROUP ACTIVITY

1. In this exercise you will examine the advantages and disadvantages of limited use garments. One half of the group should brainstorm the advantages while the other half of the group brainstorms the disadvantages. Rejoin and compare notes.

2. The selection and use of specialized protective clothing at a hazmat emergency should include an evaluation of the capabilities of the user/wearer. One half of the group should develop a list of physical stressors that may affect responders; the other half of the group should develop a list of the psychological stressors. Rejoin, present the lists, and discuss way to minimize the identified stressors.

STUDY GROUP LEARNING THROUGH INQUIRY SCENARIO 8-1

You are the Emergency Response Supervisor within a refinery. Among the various processes within the refinery is a hydrofluoric acid alkylation (HF alky) unit. An emergency at the HF Alky Unit could potentially involve a wide range of mixtures of toxic hydrofluoric acid (HF) or flammable liquefied petroleum gas (LPG). Depending upon the nature of the incident and the location of a release, you could be faced with a situation ranging from 100% LPG, to a 50% LPG / 50% HF mixture, to 100% HF.

As part of developing a pre-incident plan for the unit, respond to the following personal protective clothing issues:

1) What types of chemical protective clothing would be compatible with the hydrofluoric acid? (Review pages 353–357 and 367–377.)

2) What would your protective clothing recommendations be for the following scenarios:
   - Release of 100% HF acid as a result of a line break during a transfer operation from a tank truck to the HF storage tank.
   - Fire and release from a 2-inch pipe flange with approximately 75% LPG and 25% HF.
   - Fire from an LPG line on the unit.

3) What are the advantages and limitations of combining chemical protective clothing and thermal protective clothing into a single ensemble?

4) Assume that your ERT responded to an incident where 75% LPG and 25% HF were involved. A member from your ERT was burned when the leak ignited. He was wearing a chemically compatible Level A fully encapsulating suit at the time of injury. In your opinion, was the ERT member wearing the correct type of PPE for the hazards present? If you answered no, do you think that OSHA would be justified in issuing a citation for failure to wear the proper protective clothing? As an Incident Commander working for an oil company, do you think that you could be held liable in a civil suit brought against you by the burned ERT member?

STUDY GROUP LEARNING THROUGH INQUIRY SCENARIO 8-2

You are a fire officer assigned to an engine company in a municipal fire department. You are responding to a report of an odor in the vicinity of the Acme Ice Plant. While responding to the call, your dispatcher informs you that they have just received a 911 call for an ammonia leak inside the Ice Plant. A man is reported trapped. The assignment is upgraded which includes three engine companies, a ladder company, a rescue squad, a BLS ambulance, and the HMRT. You are first-due and about three minutes ahead of the second-due company.

You arrive on the scene and position upwind of the incident. There are about 10 employees standing outside in the parking lot. Some have been exposed to the ammonia and are having difficulty breathing. Two people are vomiting.

A supervisor from the Ice Plant frantically explains that a maintenance crew was working on a liquid refrigeration valve when something went wrong. One of the maintenance crew members did not get out and is trapped inside the building.

The Battalion Chief arrives on-scene and orders your company to don SCBA and enter the building to search for the missing worker. You have received training to the OSHA First Responder Operations Level. Although you are not that familiar with the hazards of ammonia, you know from a recent training class with the HMRT that it is toxic by inhalation, a skin irritant, and potentially explosive when released in confined areas. Your PPE meets the requirements of NFPA 1500, and consists of fire retardant structural firefighting clothing with full length pants, coat, hood, helmet, boots, gloves, and a PASS device.

Based on this situation and the information provided in Chapter 8, answer the following questions:

1) What are the hazards of ammonia? In your opinion, what is the level of risk based on the situation as it has been presented to you?

2) Are you wearing the proper type and level of protective clothing and equipment to enter the building and conduct search and rescue operations? If you answered yes, explain why. If you answered the question no, what would be the proper type of protective clothing and equipment?

3) How do you feel about the Battalion Chief's order to enter the building for search and rescue? Is this a reasonable order? If you believe that this is an unreasonable order, would you obey and enter the building even if you believed that your crew was being placed at an unreasonable risk?

4) How would you approach the Battalion Chief if you felt the risk was unreasonable? What would the consequences be if you refused to enter the building and the trapped

maintenance worker died? What if you entered the building and a member of your crew died? What if nobody died, the rescue was successful, and your crew was awarded a Unit Citation for Heroism. Would this change your opinion about taking the risk? If so, why?

SUMMARY AND REVIEW

1. Which of the following terms is defined as the physical destruction or decomposition of a clothing material due to exposure to chemicals, use, or ambient conditions:
   a. Disintegration
   b. Degradation
   c. Diffusion
   d. Degeneration

2. List at least two visible signs of degradation:

3. Penetration resistance data are provided as:
   a. "Pass" or "fail"
   b. >480 minutes or >8 hours
   c. .mg/cm^2/min
   d. Grade A, B, or C

4. Breakthrough time is defined as:
   a. The time it takes a hazardous chemical to physically destroy or decompose the chemical protective clothing material
   b. The rate at which the chemical passes through the chemical protective clothing material
   c. The time from the initial chemical attack on the outside of the material until its desorption and detection inside.
   d. The rate of flow or movement of a hazardous chemical through closures, seams, porous materials, and pinholes or other imperfections in the material

5. How can you tell if an article of protective clothing is NFPA compliant?

6. Why isn't degradation or immersion testing considered sufficient for compatibility assessment?

7. List at least two advantages of using SCBA:

8. List at least two disadvantages or limitations of using SCBA:

9. Assume that you have an IDLH atmosphere and no secondary emergency air supply. Which of the following respiratory protection should you select:
   a. APR (air purification respirator)
   b. PAPR (powered-air purification respirator)
   c. SCBA (self-contained breathing apparatus)
   d. SAR (supplied air respirator)

10. Structural firefighting clothing (SFC) is normally not the first PPE choice for most hazmat response scenarios, except when the incident involves:
   a. Corrosives and PCBs
   b. Cyanide compounds
   c. Infectious bloodborne diseases
   d. Flammable gas and liquid fire incidents

11. According to research conducted by the U.S. Army Research, Development, and Engineering Command (RDECOM), firefighters using standard turnout gear and SCBA to perform rescue of known live victims can operate in a nerve agent vapor hazard for up to 30 minutes with minimal risks associated with nerve agent exposure. What are the risks associated with these 30-minute operations?

12. In emergency response, liquid chemical splash protective clothing is often used for initial response operations. Identify at least one other operation in which liquid chemical splash protective clothing is used:

13. Identify one advantage of selecting a chemical vapor suit with a supplied air respirator.

14. True or False: Proximity suits are not designed to offer any substantial chemical protection

15. Procedures for donning and doffing of specific CPC ensembles should be based upon:
    a. NFPA 1991 or NFPA 1992
    b. Manufacturer's instructions
    c. NIOSH Pocket Guide recommendations
    d. Environmental conditions (i.e., weather, noise, etc.)

SUMMARY AND REVIEW ANSWER KEY

1. b. Degradation (p. 353)

2. To be correct, your answer should include at least two of the following: charring, shrinking, swelling, color change or dissolving (p. 353)

3. a. "Pass" or "fail" (p. 354)

4. c. The time from the initial chemical attack on the outside of the material until its desorption and detection inside. (p. 355)

5. Compliant products must carry a product label indicating compliance with the NFPA standard. (p. 360)

6. Because permeation of rubber or plastic fabrics can occur with little or no physical effect on the clothing material. Remember, permeation is an insidious process that can occur with no sign of degradation. (p. 363)

7. To be correct, your answer should include at least two of the following::
    - Readily available in the emergency response community
    - Most responders are proficient in their use
    - SCBA provide the highest level of respiratory protection (p. 367)

8. To be correct, your answer should include at least two of the following:
    - Size, weight, bulkiness
    - Limited duration of air supply
    - Overall resistance of the SCBA and its components to chemical exposures
    - Size restrictions when used in confined spaces (p. 367)

9. c. SCBA (self-contained breathing apparatus) (p. 368)

10. d. Flammable gas and liquid fire incidents (p.370)

11. 50% of firefighters may experience increased sweating and muscle weakness 1–18 hours after exposure. (p. 373)

12. Liquid chemical splash protective clothing is often used to protect decon personnel, and for postemergency response investigation and clean-up operations. (p. 374)

13. To be correct, your answer should include at least one of the following:

- Permits extended operations.
- Positive pressure always maintained in the suit.
- Airline hose may provide mechanism for minor body cooling.
- May rely upon SCBA as primary air supply and airline hose or a second SCBA bottle as secondary air supply. (p. 377)

14. True (p. 380)

15. b. Manufacturer's instructions (p.386)

Crossword Answer Key:

Across		**Down**	
2.	PNA	1.	Hazmat
5.	SAR	2.	PAPR
7.	SEI	3.	ARFF
8.	MDPR	4.	NIOSH
9.	CPC	6.	PVC
10.	HMRT	7.	SFC

SELF EVALUATION

Please review all your work in this lesson. Now that you have completed this lesson, please take about 15 minutes to note your stronger and weaker areas.

Overall I feel I did (very well / well / fair / not so well) on the acronyms and abbreviations exercise.

Overall I feel I did (very well / well / fair / not so well) on the self-test questions.

Overall I feel I did (very well / well / fair / not so well) on the summary and review questions.

When compared to the previous lessons, I think I performed (better / worse / equally well).

List two areas in Chapter 8 in which you feel you could improve your skill or knowledge level:

1.

2.

Consider the following self-evaluation questions as they pertain to Chapter 8:
Am I taking effective margin notes?

Am I dedicating enough quality time to my studies?

Is anything distracting my focus?

Was any part of Chapter 8 too advanced for me?

Did I find that I don't have enough background experience to sufficiently grasp certain subject areas?

For areas in which I did particularly well, was it because I'm particularly interested in that subject matter? How so?

Were some things easier to learn because I have prior experience in learning or working with the concepts or principles?

Did I find that certain portions of the textbook seem to be better organized and effective in explaining key points?

What other Students have had to say about Chapter 8 material:

> " The subject area that can be the most challenging is protective clothing. You MUST have a very good research team that can tell you what suits an entry team can use to ensure proper safety.
>
> Selecting the appropriate protective equipment is the trickiest. It requires proper cross checking of data. The last thing you want is your PPE to go wobbly because you didn't verify its resistance to the spilled chemical.
>
> I think that many times, we become complacent with the use of PPE. To quote a line that was in our text - PPE is not our first line of defense against the hazard - it could be our last line of defense.
>
> The ability to select the proper PPE for the specific hazard could make the difference between life or death."

Pat on the Back

Congratulations on working though Chapter 8 in the textbook and for completing the exercises in this lesson.

CHAPTER 9

INFORMATION MANAGEMENT AND RESOURCE COORDINATION

CHAPTER ORIENTATION

Open the text to page 394. Take about 10 minutes to skim the chapter. Pay attention to the boldface subject headings. Read the titles to all the figures and note how they fit into the subject headings. Scan the case studies. Please read the introduction and summary sections carefully. When you have finished looking through Chapter 9, respond to the following items. Please use the textbook as you jot down your comments in the spaces provided below:

1. What would you say is the key to coordinating information and resources required to resolve a working hazmat emergency?

2. Reflect on your current level of knowledge or background experience about the topics covered in Chapter 9. Where have you read about, learned about, or applied this knowledge in the past?

3. What sections or parts of Chapter 9 strike you as looking especially interesting?

4. What particular subjects in this chapter are important for a person in your position to master?

5. What do you predict will be the hardest things for you to learn in this chapter?

LEARNING OBJECTIVES

Turn to page 394 and examine the chapter objectives. When you have finished, respond to the following question:

1. Which objectives in Chapter 9 do you feel you can achieve right now, with a reasonable level of confidence?

As you read the sections of the chapter that deal with the objectives you have identified above, make sure your ideas or knowledge base match those of the authors. If not, you should examine how your current understanding of the material differs from that of the authors'. Depending on the level at which you wish to master the subject, discrepancies will have to be rectified and gaps will need to be filled.

ABBREVIATIONS AND ACRONYMS

The following abbreviations and acronyms are used in Chapter 9:

HMRT	Hazardous Materials Response Team (p. 401, 402)
EOC	Emergency Operations Center (p. 402)
IC	Incident Commander (p. 395, 405, 409, 410, 412, 413)
IAP	Incident Action Plan (p. 395, 404)
ICP	Incident Command Post (p. 412, 413)
LEPC	Local Emergency Planning Committee (p. 413)
MOU	Memorandum Of Understanding (p. 412)
OPSEC	Operations Security (p. 400)
PDA	Personal Data Assistant (p. 401)
PPE	Personal Protective Clothing and Equipment (p. 397, 403, 405, 406)

Locate these abbreviations and acronyms in the textbook (page numbers provided above) and underline them. Read the paragraph in which they are used.

PUZZLE:

(This puzzle has two steps)

Step 1: Use the word cues below to identify each acronym or abbreviation. Write the answers in the boxes:

☐◯ The individual responsible for establishing and managing the overall incident action plan.

☐☐◯◯ This organized group of employees is expected to perform work to handle and control actual or potential leaks or spills of hazardous substances requiring possible close approach to the substance.

◯☐◯ The strategic goals, tactical objectives and support requirements for the incident.

☐◯☐ Secured site where government or facility officials exercise centralized direction and control in an emergency.

Equipment provided to shield or isolate a person from the chemical, physical, and thermal hazards that may be encountered at a hazardous materials incident:

The location at which the primary command functions are executed, usually co-located with the incident base.

A handheld device that may combine many computing activities.

Written agreement between different organizations that may have overlapping areas of responsibility.

Serves as a focal point in the community for information and discussions about hazardous substances, emergency planning, and health and environmental risks.

Step 2: Take the letters you have written in the circle-boxes above and unscramble them to reveal the term below:

								N	S

S				R		T	Y

The puzzle Answer Key is at the end of this chapter.

STUDY SESSION OVERVIEW

Read pages 394 to the top of page 402, then take a short break to think about what you have read. Then read the rest of the chapter. Take margin notes as you go. Underline or highlight phrases that you feel are important.

When you have completed your reading, respond to the following questions. You may use the textbook to help you answer the questions, or work from memory.

1. In your own words and using examples, explain how accurate, effective, and timely information management and resource coordination is essential to:

   a) Safety of responders

b) Development of the IC's Incident Action Plan

2. In your own words and using examples, explain how poor or ineffective information management and resource coordination can politically damage the IC's credibility and ultimately undermine the response operation:

3. According to the text on page 413, most resource coordination problems fall into three categories:

   - Failure to understand or work within the IMS structure
   - Given the type and nature of the incident, failure to anticipate potential problems and "gaps" in information or resources
   - Communications and personality problems between the players

   Based on your own experience, which of these occur most frequently? Which has the potential to create the greatest problems? Give some examples.

SELF-TEST

Answer the following questions. You may use the textbook to help you answer the questions, or work from memory.

1. Specific gravity, flash point, exposures values, and vapor density are all examples of [p. 395]
   a. Data
   b. Facts
   c. Information
   d. Opinion

2. Statements made or observations about something that has occurred and has been verified and validated as being true are:

   [p. 396]

   a. Data
   b. Facts
   c. Information
   d Opinion

3. True or False: Information management must begin well before the incident.

   [p. 397]

4. Which of the following is a common mistake made at the emergency scene regarding data:

   [p. 396]

   a. Looking up the wrong chemical in the data base
   b. Not copying the information down correctly
   c. Failure to validate the data using another reference source
   d. All of the above

5. To be useful, pre-planning documents must be:

   [p. 400]

   a. Available online for easy and rapid access
   b. Completed using a standardized format
   c. Prepared in as much detail as possible, including maps and photographs
   d. Prepared by objective, third-party persons who will not normally respond to emergencies at pre-planned facilities

6. When a Hazmat Group is organized within the ICS, the responsibility for hazmat information is usually delegated to the:

   [p. 402]

   a. Hazmat Group Supervisor
   b. Logistics Section Chief
   c. Liaison Officer
   d. Situation Unit Leader

7. In order to be effective, checklists must be:

   [p. 404]

   a. NFPA 472 compliant
   b. Updated on a regular basis
   c. Stored electronically
   d. Standardized across all neighboring jurisdictions

8. Supply resources differ from equipment resources in the supply resources are:
   [p. 404]
   a. Less expensive
   b. Easier to requisition
   c. Expendable
   d. Don't usually require decontamination

9. Within the Hazmat Group, resources are coordinated by the:
   [p. 404]
   a. Staging Area Manager
   b. Information Officer
   c. Safety Officer
   d. Resource Leader

10. The following are all units of the Service Branch of the Logistics Section, except one:
   [p. 408]
   a. Communications
   b. Facilities
   c. Medical (ERP Rehab)
   d. Food

ANSWER KEY

Check your answers. If you missed more than two, you should read the chapter once again.

1. Specific gravity, flash point, exposures values, and vapor density are all examples of
   [p. 395]
   a. Data
   b. Facts
   c. Information
   d. Opinion

2. Statements made or observations about something that has occurred and has been verified and validated as being true are:
   [p. 396]
   a. Data
   b. Facts
   c. Information
   d Opinion

3. **True** or False: Information management must begin well before the incident.
   [p. 397]

4. Which of the following is a common mistake made at the emergency scene regarding data:

[p. 396]

a. Looking up the wrong chemical in the data base

b. Not copying the information down correctly

c. Failure to validate the data using another reference source

d. All of the above

5. To be useful, pre-planning documents must be:

[p. 400]

a. Available online for easy and rapid access

b. Completed using a standardized format

c. Prepared in as much detail as possible, including maps and photographs

d. Prepared by objective, third-party persons who will not normally respond to emergencies at pre-planned facilities

6. When a Hazmat Group is organized within the ICS, the responsibility for hazmat information is usually delegated to the:

[p. 402]

a. Hazmat Group Supervisor

b. Logistics Section Chief

c. Liaison Officer

d. Situation Unit Leader

7. In order to be effective, checklists must be:

[p. 404]

a. NFPA 472 compliant

b. Updated on a regular basis

c. Stored electronically

d. Standardized across all neighboring jurisdictions

8. Supply resources differ from equipment resources in the supply resources are:

[p. 404]

a. Less expensive

b. Easier to requisition

c. Expendable

d. Don't usually require decontamination

9. Within the Hazmat Group, resources are coordinated by the:

[p. 404]

a. Staging Area Manager

b. Information Officer

c. Safety Officer

d. Resource Leader

10. The following are all units of the Service Branch of the Logistics Section, except one: [p. 408]
    a. Communications
    b. Facilities
    c. Medical (ERP Rehab)
    d. Food

PRACTICE

1. What makes you suspect that the data provided below on chlorine is not correct? What should you do to verify this data?

CHLORINE	**Hazard Rating = High**
	Fire Hazard Index = 3
CAS NO. 7774-50-5	Health Hazard Index = 3
UN/NA NO. 1017	Reactivity Hazard Index = 1

PRODUCT NAME : Chlorine

SPECIAL HAZARDS: Chlorine is an extremely poisonous gas and is toxic by inhalation. It is a strong oxidizer and may react explosively or form explosive compounds with many common chemicals, such as hydrocarbons.

PHYSICAL AND CHEMICAL CHARACTERISTICS:

EXPOSURE VALUES:	TLV/TWA = 0.5 ppm: OSHA PEL = 0.5 ppm: STEL = 1 ppm: IDLH = 30 ppm.
FLASH POINT:	Not applicable
FLAMMABLE LIMITS (% by Volume):	Not applicable
AUTOIGNITION TEMPERATURE:	Not applicable
BOILING POINT:	-29°F
SPECIFIC GRAVITY:	1.4 @ 68°F
VAPOR DENSITY:	2.5 @ -30°F

2. Use Scan 9-A on page 399 to answer the following questions:

   a) You are looking for information on Tank 142 in the West Plant. Do you have the correct procedure?

   b) What Pre-plan Section addressed dike fires?

   c) Tank 142 has what kind of fixed fire protection?

   d) Where is Tractor 4 located?

3. Go to http://www.8stepprocess.com and read the OPSEC monograph located in the Chapter 9 link, "Information Management and Resource Coordination." Using an OPSEC frame-of-reference, examine the methods in which your organization's pre-plans are stored and accessed. Prepare a brief that suggests ways in which your organization can better protect pre-planning information.

4. You have been assigned to write a proposal to obtain a set of published emergency response references, including reference manuals and guidebooks, online databases and information websites, and a listing of technical information centers. Conduct the necessary background research and develop your proposal. Note: Your proposal should include an evaluation of each reference in terms of value, usefulness, and applicability to hazards and risks in your jurisdiction, user friendliness, durability, accessibility, and other similar factors. Be sure to specify special equipment or training that will be needed to access or use the references. Your proposal should be comprehensive, realistic, and justifiable.

5. For purposes of this scenario, assume that you are the Incident Commander.

   On a Thursday morning in May at 11:00 a.m. your fire department responds to a report of a fire at a metal processing plant. What information do you need prior to and upon arrival at the scene?

The foreman who reported the fire tells you he smelled rubber burning, but when he went to investigate he could not see through the smoke. Based on this initial report, do you have data, facts, or opinion?

Size-up confirms a large fire in the processing area. The pre-plan indicates that sulfuric acid is your primary concern. What are your information needs at this point? What resources will you use to get the information you require?

6. Based on your own experience, identify some of the advantages you have found in using a checklist system for coordinating and managing information in the field. The compare your list with those advantages provided on page 403-404 in the textbook.

7. What skills and abilities are needed to perform in the role of the Hazmat Information Officer (INFO)? Under what conditions would you feel qualified to function in this role?

8. For purposes of this scenario, assume that you are the Incident Commander at an airport.

   At 8 a.m. you receive a dispatch to the International Terminal where more than 100 people are reported to be experiencing dizziness, nausea, vomiting, and respiratory distress. No fires have been detected and an unconfirmed report said that there was no noticeable odors or smoke. Based on this limited information, what human, equipment, and supply resources do you anticipate needing for the first hour of this response?

9. Go to http://www.8stepprocess.com for additional information and activities pertaining to Chapter 9 "Information Management and Resource Coordination."

STUDY GROUP ACTIVITY

1. One member in the group should relate a personal experience at a hazmat incident in which he or she was initially overwhelmed by the quantity of incoming information. As a group, discuss the scenario and suggest ways in which the problem with information overload could have been better managed.

2. Using the criteria listed on page 400 and presented below, group members should identify problem areas in their own jurisdiction that may require special pre-planning:
   - Type of hazards and risks present
   - Environmentally sensitive exposures
   - Unusual or poor water supply requirements

- Locations that will require large quantities of foam concentrate
- Restricted or delayed response routes
- Poor accessibility

3. As a group, design a template that can be used for pre-planning key transportation areas in your jurisdiction.

4. As a group, identify potential problems that could be encountered with electronic information storage and retrieval under a variety of conditions. Then brainstorm solutions and work-arounds.

STUDY GROUP LEARNING THROUGH INQUIRY SCENARIO 9-1

Your Chief has asked you to develop recommendations for information management improvement to the new hazardous materials response unit that is being designed. The chief is a "gadget" kind of guy and he wants the new unit to be state-of-the art with the latest communications and computer equipment. He wants "everything paperless" on the new unit.

1) What criteria will you use to develop your information management specifications? (Review pages 396 to 400, Chapter 9.)

2) Based on your research you have determined that the Chief's idea of being completely automated and "paperless" is not the best course of action. How would you make your case that there should be some redundancy in your information management system? What references would you carry as Hard Copy vs. Soft Copy? (See pages 401–402, Chapter 9.)

3) What are the advantages of using checklists as a method of coordinating information at the incident scene?

STUDY GROUP LEARNING THROUGH INQUIRY SCENARIO 9-2

You are the on-duty acting military shift supervisor at a U.S. Air Force base fire department. You are a Technical Sergeant (E-6) with eight years experience. It is a holiday and there is very limited activity on the base. At 5:45 PM you receive an emergency call for a fuel spill inside of a hangar on the flightline. You respond with three Aircraft Rescue/Firefighting (ARFF) vehicles and a structural engine company.

When you arrive on the scene you find an F-16 fighter parked inside the hangar with about 10 gallons of jet fuel pooled on the hangar floor. The door is open on the hangar and there are several maintenance vehicles parked inside. You take a combustible gas indicator reading near the hangar door and determine that the atmosphere at floor level is approximately 80% of the LEL. You have ordered that the area be isolated and ignition sources secured, however, your prefire plan does not indicate where the overhead heating system master switch is located. You are very concerned about a fire and explosion.

There is no fixed foam system inside the hangar. You make the decision to foam the fuel spill down as a way to reduce the vapors and reduce the potential for an explosion inside the hangar. You are well aware of both the aircraft replacement costs and maintenance costs associated with your actions.

As you begin foaming down the fuel spill under the aircraft, the Maintenance Supervisor shows up. He outranks you as a First Lieutenant and expresses his opinion that it is a waste of time and money to foam down the spill. He doesn't want to make a big mess inside the hangar, and wants to use fire department and maintenance personnel to manually tow the aircraft outside of the hangar. You feel that this is neither safe nor practical.

Even though the First Lieutenant outranks you, you know that Air Force regulations place the emergency on-scene commander in charge of fire and rescue operations regardless of rank. In other words, you would be within your authority to foam the spill down regardless of the Maintenance Supervisor's objections. However, for obvious chain-of-command and career reasons, you don't want this situation to turn into a major political incident. This is also your first time as acting shift officer, and you don't want to blow any potential career opportunities.

Based on the background information provided and information in Chapter 9, answer the following questions:

1) What type of resources would you need to safely mitigate this incident? Be specific and list both the equipment and human resources required.

2) In your opinion, what is the fundamental problem with this situation from an Information and Resource Coordination perspective?

3) The Maintenance Supervisor is presenting a major political problem for you. This problem has the potential to become a major issue within the military chain-of-command if you handle it incorrectly. How would you resolve his concerns? Refer to page 413 in the text and review the model solutions provided for resolving conflict. Which techniques would be most effective in helping you avoid a major conflict with the Officer?

SUMMARY AND REVIEW

1. Fill in the blank:

   DATA + ______________ = INFORMATION

2. Information management must begin well <u>before</u> the incident. For example, what type of information will be needed at the scene? How should the information be complied? Identify at least one other information management question that should be answered before an incident occurs:

3. One way to deal with information overload is to distinguish between information we need to know versus information that is nice to know. For example, we need to know what the hazards of the materials are and what the PPE requirements are. Identify at least two other "need-to-know" pieces of information:

4. There are several information sources that should be immediately accessible from the incident scene, such as pre-incident tactical plans. Identify at least one other source of information:

5. What kinds of information can be found in a facility emergency response plan:

6. What kinds of facilities will most certainly present accessibility problems to responding units and must be pre-planned?

7. Resources are made up of people, equipment and supplies. For each of the following resources, identify at least one support need:

People:

Vehicles:

Generators:

8. Fill in the boxes on the left hand side of the following organizational chart:

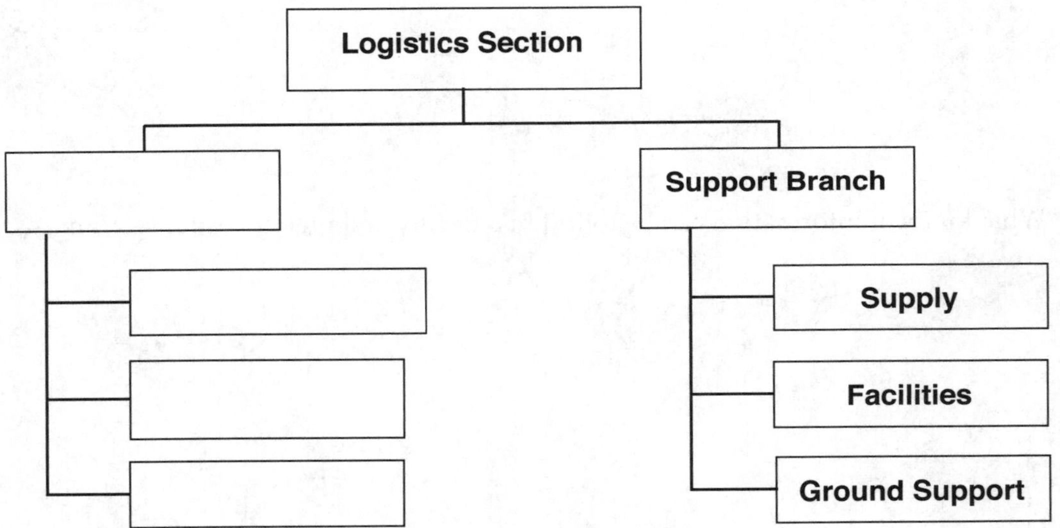

9. Most emergency response organizations call on the same cast of external players on a regular basis. What is the best way to ensure that these external resources will be properly coordinated and integrated into your command structure?

SUMMARY AND REVIEW ANSWER KEY

1. DATA + FACTS = INFORMATION (p. 396)

2. To be correct, your answer should include at least one of the following:
   - What is the priority of the information that is needed? What do you need immediately versus an hour into the incident?
   - How will the information be stored for quick recovery at the incident scene – manually or electronically?
   - Are the information and retrieval systems suitable for field applications?
   - Who will be responsible for managing and coordinating information at the incident scene? Are they properly trained and equipped for the job? (p. 397)

3. To be correct, your answer should include at least two of the following:
   - What are the health concerns (e.g., exposure values, signs and symptoms of exposure, antidotes, etc.)?
   - What is the container type and condition (integrity, size, orientations etc.)?
   - What are the initial tactical recommendations (e.g., spill control, leak control, fire control, public protective actions)?
   - What type of decontamination procedures and methods will be required? (p. 398)

4. To be correct, your answer should include at least one of the following:
   - Facility emergency response plans
   - Published emergency response references
   - Shipping documents (p. 398)

5. These plans usually have a hazard analysis section, which identifies special problems that may exist within the plant or community, the potential risks and consequences of a hazmat incident, and the available emergency response resources in the facility. (p. 398.

6. Secure government installations with strong antiterrorism force protection countermeasures in place. (p. 400)

7. People: Food and water, toilet facilities, rehab facilities

   Vehicles: Diesel fuel, oil

   Generators: Gasoline or diesel fuel (p. 408)

8.

- **Service Branch**
  - **Communications**
  - **Medical (ERP Rehab)**
  - **Ground Support**

(p. 408)

9. The best way to guarantee that external resources are properly coordinated into your command structure is to develop written guidelines or memorandums of understanding (MOUs) between your respective organizations. (p. 412)

Puzzle Answer Key:

IC

HMRT

IAP

EOC

PPE

ICP

PDA

MOU

LEPC

Operations Security

SELF EVALUATION

Please review all your work in this lesson. Now that you have completed this lesson, please take about 15 minutes to note your stronger and weaker areas.

Overall I feel I did (very well / well / fair / not so well) on the acronyms and abbreviations exercise.

Overall I feel I did (very well / well / fair / not so well) on the self-test questions.

Overall I feel I did (very well / well / fair / not so well) on the summary and review questions.

When compared to the previous lessons, I think I performed (better / worse / equally well).

List two areas in Chapter 9 in which you feel you could improve your skill or knowledge level:

1.

2.

Consider the following self-evaluation questions as they pertain to Chapter 9:

Am I taking effective margin notes?

Am I dedicating enough quality time to my studies?

Is anything distracting my focus?

Was any part of Chapter 9 too advanced for me?

Did I find that I don't have enough background experience to sufficiently grasp certain subject areas?

For areas in which I did particularly well, was it because I'm particularly interested in that subject matter? How so?

Were some things easier to learn because I have prior experience in learning or working with the concepts or principles?

Did I find that certain portions of the textbook seem to be better organized and effective in explaining key points?

What other Students have had to say about Chapter 9 material:

"The operational aspect of this chapter is very important for me as a hamat technician. Information and resource coordination is essential to effectively mitigating an incident with no additional harm caused to responders or civilians/victims.

To prepare myself for promotion to Captain I need to master the ability to properly institute pre-planned procedures, and be able to properly manage and coordinate resources at an incident. I continue to try to learn as much as possible.

I understand the importance of this subject and where it fits in with the overall incident management but because it involves so many different moving parts and because I have not had much if any experience doing this, I know I would find this chapter challenging.

There appears to be so many methods of hazard data collection and information dissemination, one doesn't know where to begin. I think the key is to be focused in your info gathering so as to obtain the most pertinent and critical information possible. Computer databases can also be a good tool in gathering this info.

My department recently purchased a laptop computer to keep in our command unit to be used on hazardous materials incidents and other large incidents. Since I am in charge of all of the computers for the department and I have quite a bit of hazardous materials training compared to other people in the department, it is very likely that I could be the Information Officer on a hazardous materials incident. Therefore, information management and resource coordination are important subject areas for me to master.

Information is very important during a hazmat incident. Having the right information at the right time can help to make those plans to control the incident. Taking the time to gather information and make plans will help to prevent injuries and deaths."

Pat on the Back

Congratulations on working though Chapter 9 in the textbook and for completing the exercises in this lesson.

CHAPTER 10
IMPLEMENTING RESPONSE OBJECTIVES

CHAPTER ORIENTATION

Open the text to page 418. Take about 10 minutes to skim the chapter. Pay attention to the boldface subject headings. Read the titles to all the figures and note how they fit into the subject headings. Scan the case studies. Please read the introduction and summary sections carefully. When you have finished looking through Chapter 10, respond to the following items. Please use the textbook as you jot down your comments in the spaces provided below:

1. In one or two sentences, what is this chapter about?

2. Reflect on your current level of knowledge or background experience about the topics covered in Chapter 10. Where have you read about, learned about, or applied this knowledge in the past?

3. What sections or parts of Chapter 10 strike you as looking especially interesting?

4. What particular subjects in this chapter are important for a person in your position to master?

5. What do you predict will be the hardest things for you to learn in this chapter?

LEARNING OBJECTIVES

Turn to pages 418-420 and examine the chapter objectives. When you have finished, respond to the following question:

1. Which objectives in Chapter 10 do you feel you can achieve right now, with a reasonable level of confidence?

Highlight or place a check mark next to those objectives on pages 418-420 that addresses educational competencies referenced in *NFPA 472—Professional Competence of Responders to Hazardous Materials*.

As you read the sections of the chapter that deal with the objectives you have identified above, make sure your ideas or knowledge base match those of the authors. If not, you should examine how your current understanding of the material differs from that of the authors'. Depending on the level at which you wish to master the subject, discrepancies will have to be rectified and gaps will need to be filled.

ABBREVIATIONS AND ACRONYMS

The following abbreviations and acronyms are used in Chapter 10:

AFFF	Aqueous Film Forming Foam (p. 460, 461, 462, 463, 468, 469)
ARC	Alcohol Resistant Concentrate (p. 461, 465, 466)
ARFF	Aircraft Rescue Firefighting (p. 456)

ASME	American Society of Mechanical Engineers (p. 477, 493)
BLEVE	Boiling Liquid Expanding Vapor Explosion (p. 424, 472, 474, 475, 476, 477)
CNG	Compressed Natural Gas (p. 472)
FFFP	Film Forming Fluoroprotein Foam (p. 462, 463)
LPG	Liquefied Petroleum Gas (p. 424, 443, 472, 475, 476, 477, 492)
MOTEL	Magnitude, Occurrence, Timing, Effects and Location (p. 422)
NTSB	National Transportation Safety Board (p. 421, 422, 476)
pH	Power of Hydrogen (p. 439, 440, 445)
PPE	Personal Protective Clothing and Equipment (p. 427, 433, 435, 484, 493)

Locate these abbreviations and acronyms in the textbook (page numbers provided above) and underline them. Read the paragraph in which they are used.

Fill in the blank using the abbreviations and acronyms above.

1. Provides measure of acidity or alkalinity of a solution: ______

2. When applied to a polar solvent fuel, will often create a polymeric membrane rather than a film over the fuel: ______

3. Federal group responsible for investigating major transportation disasters: ______

4. Shields a person from the chemical, physical, and thermal hazards that may be encountered at a hazardous materials incident: ______

5. Often accompanied by a large fireball if a flammable gas is involved: ______

6. Sets industry and manufacturing codes and standards that enhance public safety: ______

7. Firefighting related to airport operations and aircraft safety: ______

8. Synthetic Class B firefighting foam consisting of fluorochemical and hydrocarbon surfactants: ______

9. Class B firefighting foam based on fluoroprotein foam: ______

10. Acronym for the five factors that should be evaluated by the IC in order to influence the outcome of the emergency: ______

11. A mixture of butane, propane and other light hydrocarbons derived from refining crude oil: ______

12. Natural gas (methane) after being compressed for storage in pressure vessels: ______

ANSWER KEY

1. Provides measure of acidity or alkalinity of a solution: pH
2. When applied to a polar solvent fuel, will often create a polymeric membrane rather than a film over the fuel: ARC
3. Federal group responsible for investigating major transportation disasters: NTSB
4. Shields a person from the chemical, physical, and thermal hazards that may be encountered at a hazardous materials incident: PPE
5. Often accompanied by a large fireball if a flammable gas is involved: BLEVE
6. Sets industry and manufacturing codes and standards that enhance public safety: ASME
7. Firefighting related to airport operations and aircraft safety: ARFF
8. Synthetic Class B firefighting foam consisting of fluorochemical and hydrocarbon surfactants: AFFF
9. Class B firefighting foam based on fluoroprotein foam: FFFP
10. Acronym for the five factors that should be evaluated by the IC in order to influence the outcome of the emergency: MOTEL
11. A mixture of butane, propane and other light hydrocarbons derived from refining crude oil: LPG
12. Natural gas (methane) after being compressed for storage in pressure vessels: CNG

STUDY SESSION OVERVIEW

Read pages 420 to the middle of page 454, then take a short break to think about what you have read. Then read the rest of the chapter. Take margin notes as you go. Underline or highlight phrases that you feel are important.

When you have completed your reading, respond to the following questions. You may use the textbook to help you answer the questions, or work from memory.

1. There has been a significant reduction in the number of hazmat incidents resulting in multiple fatalities and casualties over the last two decades. According to Chapter 10, what is one of the primary reasons for this reduction?

2. In your own words, explain the concept of the emergency timeline, and explain its value in determining which strategy and tactics are best suited to change the outcome for a hazmat incident.

3. Although offensive operations can increase the risk to emergency responders, when may the risk be justified?

4. Some tactics can be employed to delay events or slow down the clock until entry teams are ready to implement the "final solution." Give an example of a tactical option that could be used to buy time and explain how it would work:

5. What makes technical rescue problems involving hazmats difficult to plan for and execute?

6. What are some of the advantages of conducting confinement operations over containment operations?

7. What are the role and activities of public safety responders during product transfer and removal operations?

SELF-TEST

Answer the following questions. You may use the textbook to help you answer the questions, or work from memory.

1. The following statements all pertain to *strategy*, except one:
   [p. 423]
   a. A strategy is a plan for managing resources
   b. A strategy is usually very broad in nature
   c. A strategy is selected at the Command Level
   d. Only one strategy should be pursued at a time during an incident

2. The following statements all pertain to *tactics*, except one:
   [p. 424]
   a. Tactics are specific objectives used to achieve strategic goals
   b. Tactics are normally decided at the section or group/division levels in the command structure
   c. Tactics are rarely or never implemented when operating in the nonintervention mode
   d. Several tactics may be implemented simultaneously during an incident

3. Nonintervention means taking no action other than:
   [p. 424]
   a. Rescue
   b. Isolating the area
   c. Defensive public protective actions
   d. Incident stabilization

4. The specific activities that accomplish a tactical objective are called:
   [p. 425]
   a. Operations
   b. Tasks
   c. Procedures
   d. Priorities

5. With regard to the "First Law of Hot Zone Operations," assume you are "trained to play, dressed to play, and using the buddy system; you have a back-up capability and an emergency decon capability, but you don't have command approval for the entry rescue operation. Can you work in the hot zone? Yes / No (p. 429-430)

6. Technical rescue includes rescue of one or more victims who have been exposed to the hazmat and require:
[p. 430]
   a. Triage
   b. Immediate relocation
   c. Physical extrication
   d. Treatment

7. The following are all examples of confined spaces, as defined by OSHA, except one:
[p. 432]
   a. Aircraft cockpit
   b. Rail car
   c. Boiler
   d. Pipeline

Match each confinement tactical option in Column A to its description or definition in Column B.

Column A Confinement Tactic	Column B Description/Definition
8.______Absorption (p. 436)	A. Constructing a barrier across a waterway to stop/control the product flow and pick up the liquid or solid contaminants.
9.______Adsorption (p. 436)	B. Chemical method by which a water-soluble solution, usually a corrosive, is diluted by adding large volumes of water to the spill.
10.______Covering (p. 437)	C. Barriers are constructed on ground or placed in a waterway to intentionally control the movement of a hazardous material into an area where it will pose less harm to the community and the environment.
11.______Damming (p. 437)	D. Fans or water spray is used to disperse or move vapors away from certain areas or materials.
12.______Diking (p. 438)	E. Physical process of absorbing or "picking up" a liquid hazmat to prevent enlargement of the contaminated area.
13.______Dilution (p. 438)	F. Physical method of confinement to reduce or eliminate the vapors emanating from a spilled or released material.
14.______Diversion (p. 440)	G. Placing a tarp over a spill of dust or powder
15.______Dispersion (p. 441)	H. Involves placing a material or device over a breach to keep the hazmat inside of the container.
16.______Retention (p. 441)	I. The chemical process in which a sorbate (liquid hazardous material) interacts with a solid sorbent sur face.

17._______Vapor dispersion (p. 441)

18._______Vapor suppression (p. 442)

J. A liquid is temporarily contained in an area where it can be absorbed, neutralized, or picked up for proper disposal.

K. Chemical and biological agents are used to disperse or break up the material involved in liquid spills on water.

L. Barriers are constructed on ground used to control the movement of liquids, sludges, solids, or other materials.

19. The following are all physical methods of confinement, except one: [p. 441]
    a. Covering
    b. Damming
    c. Dispersion
    d. Vapor suppression

20. Which of the following confinement tactics should be used only when all other reasonable methods of mitigation and removal have proven unacceptable: [p. 439]
    a. Dilution
    b. Diversion
    c. Dispersion
    d. Covering

21. Which of the following statements about leak control strategies and containment tactics are all true, except one: [p. 442]
    a. Containment tactics are often implemented only when defensive options would be too expensive or time-consuming
    b. Containment tactics should only be approved after conducting a thorough hazard and risk evaluation.
    c. Containment tactics require personnel to enter the hot zone to control the release at its source
    d. Containment tactics should be considered high-risk operations

22. For alkali spills, the most widely favored neutralizing agent from an environmental perspective is: [p. 446]
    a. Ascorbic acid
    b. Acetic acid
    c. Hydrochloric acid
    d. Perchloric Acid

23. True or False: Overpack containers must be labeled in accordance with DOT hazmat regulations if it will be transported from the scene. [p. 447]

24. When used as a method of containment, plugs must be compatible with both the chemical and the:
[p. 448]
a. Available tools
b. Available time
c. Container
d. Atmospheric conditions

25. Which of the following is a critical factor in evaluating the application and use of patching tactics:
[p. 447]
a. Container size
b. Container pressure
c. The position of the container
d. Availability of properly rated commercial patches

26. Responders should consult with container specialists to assess the level of risk and control options for which of the following types of liquid cargo tank truck leaks:
[p. 450]
a. Valve leaks
b. MC-306/DOT-406 piping leaks
c. Liquid being released from pressure-relief devices
d. Breaches in the vapor space

27. Which of the following is a drawback of flaring to reduce or control pressure:
[p. 452]
a. Flares are designed to burn only vapor product
b. Flaring can cause dangerous pressure buildups in other locations
c. Flaring often takes a very long time to accomplish
d. Flaring can weaken the structural integrity of the container

28. Which of the following is often used to contain small releases of liquid mercury:
[p. 454]
a. Vacuuming
b. Solidification
c. Neutralization
d. Absorption

29. Which of the following tactical options is sometimes implemented when there are insufficient water supplies:
[p. 459]
a. Nonintervention
b. Offensive tactics
c. Defensive tactics
d. Defensive tactics directed only at primary exposures

30. With regard to tank firefighting, AFFF foam:
[p. 461]
a. Is available in 12% concentrations
b. Is compatible with Purple K dry chemical agent
c. Should not be used with salt water
d. Should not be used with dry chemical extinguishing agents

31. Which of the following recommends minimum foam application rates for specific fuels, foams, and applications:
[p. 463]
a. NFPA 326
b. NFPA 30
c. NFPA 11
d. NFPA 58

32. Pressure vessels should have a minimum of _____ gpm applied at the point of fire impingement:
[p. 472]
a. 250
b. 300
c. 400
d. 500

33. Which of the following is the first tactical priority for managing a flammable gas fire:
[p. 474]
a. Protect primary and secondary exposures to the fire
b. Control and extinguish secondary fires
c. Reduce the operating pressure of the line feeding the fire
d. Check for fire extension

34. Pressure-fed flammable gas fires may produce direct flame impingement on nearby vessels and cause catastrophic tank failure within ________ of exposure:
[p. 474]
a. 5 to 20 minutes
b. 20 to 30 minutes
c. 30 to 60 minutes
d. 1 to 5 hours

35. BLEVE is an acronym for Boiling Liquid ________ Vapor Explosion:
[p. 477]
a. Evaporating
b. Escaping
c. Expanding
d. Ejecting

36. True or False: Never extinguish a pressure-fed flammable gas fire unless you can control the fuel supply.

37. The following statements about the hazard and risk process for reactive chemicals are all true, except one:
[p. 480]
a. Small quantities of highly reactive chemicals can pose significant risks
b. Incidents involving reactive chemicals will typically require the expertise of technical information and product specialists who are familiar with the materials involved
c. The type of container will vary depending upon whether the chemical is a raw material, an intermediate material being used to form another chemical or product, or the finished product
d. Unlike flammable gases containers, reactive chemical containers will not have pressure relief devices

38. Product removal operations cannot commence until after the incident site is stabilized. Stabilization means:
[p. 485]
  a. All fires have been extinguished
  b. Ignition sources have been controlled
  c. All spills and leaks have been controlled
  d. All of the above

39. True or False: Bonding and grounding must be established before product removal and transfer operations can begin.

40. Gravity flow as a method of liquid product transfer is often ineffective for:
[p. 490]
  a. Liquids containing alcohol
  b. Viscous liquids
  c. Flammable liquids
  d. Corrosive liquids

41. Gas transfers are based on the basic principle that materials will naturally flow from:
[p. 491]
  a. High-pressure to low-pressure areas
  b. High elevation to low elevation
  c. High concentration to low concentration
  d. Volume to a vacuum

ANSWER KEY

1. The following statements all pertain to *strategy*, except one:
[p. 423]
  a. A strategy is a plan for managing resources
  b. A strategy is usually very broad in nature
  c. A strategy is selected at the Command Level
  d. Only one strategy should be pursued at a time during an incident

2. The following statements all pertain to *tactics*, except one:
[p. 424]
  a. Tactics are specific objectives used to achieve strategic goals
  b. Tactics are normally decided at the section or group/division levels in the command structure
  c. Tactics are rarely or never implemented when operating in the nonintervention mode
  d. Several tactics may be implemented simultaneously during an incident

3. Nonintervention means taking no action other than:
[p. 424]
  a. Rescue
  b. Isolating the area
  c. Defensive public protective actions
  d. Incident stabilization

4. The specific activities that accomplish a tactical objective are called: [p. 425]
   a. Operations
   b. Tasks
   c. Procedures
   d. Priorities

5. With regard to the "First Law of Hot Zone Operations," assume you are "trained to play, dressed to play, and using the buddy system; you have a back-up capability and an emergency decon capability, but you don't have command approval for the entry rescue operation. Can you work in the hot zone?
   Yes / **No** (p. 429-430)

6. Technical rescue includes rescue of one or more victims who have been exposed to the hazmat and require:
   [p. 430]
   a. Triage
   b. Immediate relocation
   c. Physical extrication
   d. Treatment

7. The following are all examples of confined spaces, as defined by OSHA, except one: [p. 432]
   a. Aircraft cockpit
   b. Rail car
   c. Boiler
   d. Pipeline

Match each confinement tactical option in Column A to its description or definition in Column B.

Column A Confinement Tactic	Column B Description/Definition
8. __E__ Absorption (p. 436)	A. Constructing a barrier across a waterway to stop/control the product flow and pick up the liquid or solid contaminants.
9. __I__ Adsorption (p. 436)	B. Chemical method by which a water-soluble solution, usually a corrosive, is diluted by adding large volumes of water to the spill.
10. __G__ Covering	C. Barriers are constructed on ground or placed in a waterway to intentionally control the movement of a hazardous material into an area where it will pose less harm to the community and the environment.
11. __A__ Damming (p. 437)	D. Fans or water spray is used to disperse or move vapors away from certain areas or materials.
12. __L__ Diking (p. 438)	E. Physical process of absorbing or "picking up" a liquid hazmat to prevent enlargement of the contaminated area.

13. ___B___ Dilution (p. 438)

14. ___C___ Diversion (p. 440)

15. ___K___ Dispersion (p. 441)

16. ___I___ Retention (p. 441)

17. ___D___ Vapor dispersion (p. 441)

18. ___F___ Vapor suppression (p. 442)

F. Physical method of confinement to reduce or eliminate the vapors emanating from a spilled or released material.

G. Placing a tarp over a spill of dust or powder

H. Involves placing a material or device over a breach to keep the hazmat inside of the container.

I. The chemical process in which a sorbate (liquid hazardous material) interacts with a solid sorbent surface.

J. A liquid is temporarily contained in an area where it can be absorbed, neutralized, or picked up for proper disposal.

K. Chemical and biological agents are used to disperse or break up the material involved in liquid spills on water.

L. Barriers are constructed on ground used to control the movement of liquids, sludges, solids, or other materials.

19. The following are all physical methods of confinement, except one: [p. 441]
    a. Covering
    b. Damming
    c. Dispersion
    d. Vapor suppression

20. Which of the following confinement tactics should be used only when all other reasonable methods of mitigation and removal have proven unacceptable: [p. 439]
    a. Dilution
    b. Diversion
    c. Dispersion
    d. Covering

21. Which of the following statements about leak control strategies and containment tactics are all true, except one: [p. 442]
    a. Containment tactics are often implemented only when defensive options would be too expensive or time-consuming
    b. Containment tactics should only be approved after conducting a thorough hazard and risk evaluation.
    c. Containment tactics require personnel to enter the hot zone to control the release at its source
    d. Containment tactics should be considered high-risk operations

22. For alkali spills, the most widely favored neutralizing agent from an environmental perspective is:
[p. 446]
a. Ascorbic acid
b. Acetic acid
c. Hydrochloric acid
d. Perchloric Acid

23. **True** or False: Overpack containers must be labeled in accordance with DOT hazmat regulations if it will be transported from the scene
[p. 447]

24. When used as a method of containment, plugs must be compatible with both the chemical and the:
[p. 448]
a. Available tools
b. Available time
c. Container
d. Atmospheric conditions

25. Which of the following is a critical factor in evaluating the application and use of patching tactics:
[p. 447]
a. Container size
b. Container pressure
c. The position of the container
d. Availability of properly rated commercial patches

26. Responders should consult with container specialists to assess the level of risk and control options for which of the following types of liquid cargo tank truck leaks:
[p. 450]
a. Valve leaks
b. MC-306/DOT-406 piping leaks
c. Liquid being released from pressure-relief devices
d. Breaches in the vapor space

27. Which of the following is a drawback of flaring to reduce or control pressure:
[p. 452]
a. Flares are designed to burn only vapor product
b. Flaring can cause dangerous pressure buildups in other locations
c. Flaring often takes a very long time to accomplish
d. Flaring can weaken the structural integrity of the container

28. Which of the following is often used to contain small releases of liquid mercury:
[p. 454]
a. Vacuuming
b. Solidification
c. Neutralization
d. Absorption

29. Which of the following tactical options is sometimes implemented when there are insufficient water supplies:
[p. 459]
<u>a</u>. **Nonintervention**
b. Offensive tactics
c. Defensive tactics
d. Defensive tactics directed only at primary exposures

30. With regard to tank firefighting, AFFF foam:
[p. 461]
a. Is available in 12% concentrations
<u>b</u>. **Is compatible with Purple K dry chemical agent**
c. Should not be used with salt water
d. Should not be used with dry chemical extinguishing agents

31. Which of the following recommends minimum foam application rates for specific fuels, foams, and applications:
[p. 463]
a. NFPA 326
b. NFPA 30
c. **NFPA 11**
d. NFPA 58

32. Pressure vessels should have a minimum of _____ gpm applied at the point of fire impingement:
[p. 472]
a. 250
b. 300
c. 400
<u>d</u>. **500**

33. Which of the following is the first tactical priority for managing a flammable gas fire:
[p. 474]
<u>a</u>. **Protect primary and secondary exposures to the fire**
b. Control and extinguish secondary fires
c. Reduce the operating pressure of the line feeding the fire
d. Check for fire extension

34. Pressure-fed flammable gas fires may produce direct flame impingement on nearby vessels and cause catastrophic tank failure within ________ of exposure:
[p. 474]
<u>a</u>. **5 to 20 minutes**
b. 20 to 30 minutes
c. 30 to 60 minutes
d. 1 to 5 hours

35. BLEVE is an acronym for Boiling Liquid ________ Vapor Explosion:
[p. 477]
a. Evaporating
b. Escaping

c. Expanding
d. Ejecting

36. **True** or False: Never extinguish a pressure-fed flammable gas fire unless you can control the fuel supply.

37. The following statements about the hazard and risk process for reactive chemicals are all true, except one:
[p. 480]
a. Small quantities of highly reactive chemicals can pose significant risks
b. Incidents involving reactive chemicals will typically require the expertise of technical information and product specialists who are familiar with the materials involved
c. The type of container will vary depending upon whether the chemical is a raw material, an intermediate material being used to form another chemical or product, or the finished product
d. Unlike flammable gases containers, reactive chemical containers will not have pressure relief devices

38. Product removal operations cannot commence until after the incident site is stabilized. Stabilization means:
[p. 485]
a. All fires have been extinguished
b. Ignition sources have been controlled
c. All spills and leaks have been controlled
d. All of the above

39. **True** or False: Bonding and grounding must be established before product removal and transfer operations can begin.

40. Gravity flow as a method of liquid product transfer is often ineffective for:
[p. 490]
a. Liquids containing alcohol
b. Viscous liquids
c. Flammable liquids
d. Corrosive liquids

41. Gas transfers are based on the basic principle that materials will naturally flow from:
[p. 491]
a. High-pressure to low-pressure areas
b. High elevation to low elevation
c. High concentration to low concentration
d. Volume to a vacuum

PRACTICE

1. Review the Fire Emergency Timeline presented on page 421. Using this timeline as a model, sketch and label an example of a hazardous materials emergency timeline.

2. Briefly explain and give a real-world example how each of the following defensive tactical options can help buy time until the most effective offensive tactic can be implemented:

   - Barriers:

   - Distance (i.e., separating people from the hazmat):

   - Time (i.e., reducing the duration of the release):

   - Techniques (i.e., procedures to stop the leak):

3. Develop a detailed equipment and supplies inventory for handling a wide range of hazmat incidents using confinement tactics.

4. You have approximately 30 gallons of diesel fuel that has been spilled into a fresh water lake at a marina. What containment tactic would you use? Explain why.

5. Assume you have an acid spill of approximately one gallon. The spill has a pH of 4. You want to dilute the spill to a pH of 6 for safer disposal. How many gallons of water will you need in order to do this?

6. How much soda ash (sodium carbonate) is needed to neutralize a one gallon spill of 70% sulfuric acid (specific gravity 1.8)?

7. Assume that you have a gasoline spill covering an areas 100 feet X 100 feet. You will be using Class B - 3% X 3% AFFF. You have 500 gallons of foam concentrate. Is this enough?

8. Briefly describe a scenario in which you would conduct an aggressive leak control strategy vs. a spill control strategy. Explain the factors in your scenario that would justify an offensive operation.

9. Chapter 10 presents a number of significant hazmat emergencies. If you were asked to make a conference presentation on one of the incidents, which one would you choose and why? Using the Internet and other resources, research that incident in more detail.

10. Go to http://www.8stepprocess.com for additional information and activities pertaining to Chapter 10 "Implementing Response Objectives."

STUDY GROUP ACTIVITY

1. One person in the group should present a scenario from his or her own experience (or a case study) in which one of the following added to the uncertainty of the decision-making process:

   - Conflicting or uncertain information; or
   - Conflicting or competing values

   As a group, discuss the outcome and what can be learned from the scenario.

2. Review the "Lessons from History" events presented on pages 497-498. As a group, discuss the "food for thought" questions.

STUDY GROUP LEARNING THROUGH INQUIRY SCENARIO 10-1

You respond to a flammable liquid storage tank fire at a petroleum marketing terminal. The 150 ft. internal floating roof tank was struck by lightning after being filled from a pipeline. When you arrive on the scene, you observe the following:

- The 150 ft. tank has a full surface fire and there are several small pool fires within the diked area.
- The fixed roof has been blown off into an adjoining 120 ft. diameter cone roof tank. Although the adjoining tank of #2 fuel oil is not yet burning, the side of the 40 ft. high tank has been punctured approximately 10 ft. from the top and product is flowing into the dike.
- Pre-fire plans have identified that water supplies are adequate in this area.
- There is approximately 2,500 gallons of AFFF 3%/3% firefighting foam concentrate available within 1 hour in the region. There are also numerous 1-1/2-inch and 2-1/2-inch foam handline nozzles available, although there are no foam cannons. An ARFF crash truck is available from a nearby Air National Guard (ANG) base.

Based on the background information provided and the information in Chapter 10, answer the following questions:

1) What would be your strategic goals and tactical objectives for this fire? Would you use offensive tactics and attempt to attack and extinguish the fire or use defensive tactics? Explain and justify your reason for using these tactics.
2) Do you have sufficient foam concentrate on-hand to attack and extinguish the fire? (See pages 464 to 469, Chapter 10.) If you believe that you do, how did you arrive at this conclusion? For example, if the facility operations manager does not believe that there is not enough foam available to extinguish the fire, how would you back up your opinion that there is?
3) What would the short and long term environmental, public affairs, and political risks be if the decision were made to pump out the burning tank and let the residual product burn itself out?

STUDY GROUP LEARNING THROUGH INQUIRY SCENARIO 10-2

You are the Safety Officer on the scene of an overturned tractor trailer incident on a secondary road. The truck contains a mixed load of hazardous materials in various small packages. The containers include:

- Ten (10) 50 lb. bags of fertilizer grade ammonium nitrate.
- Ten (10) 20 gallon containers of 35% concentration hydrogen peroxide.
- Twenty (20) 50 lb. bags of low grade potassium permanganate.
- Fourteen (14) 20 gallon containers of muriatic acid.
- Fifteen (15) 55 gallon drums of industrial grade floor cleaner.
- Seventeen (17) 30 lb. fiberboard containers of calcium hypochlorite.

During the incident, your HMRT entered the hazard area and overpacked two leaking containers of muriatic acid and repackaged several bags of ammonium nitrate. You are now standing by for a carrier to arrive at the scene with a hazardous materials contractor to complete off-loading the vehicle and clean-up the accident site.

Approximately 4 hours into the incident, a carrier representative arrives on the scene. Rather than hire a recognized environmental clean-up contractor, he has brought six dock workers who will be used to off-load the vehicle into another trailer.

Based on the information which has been provided and the information in Chapter 10, answer the following questions:

1) As the Safety Officer, what are your priorities at this point? Be specific and explain why the priorities you have selected are important to the overall safety of the operation.

2) Based on your priorities, are there any concerns that you have as far as clean-up is concerned? How would you express these concerns to your Incident Commander?

3) What type of questions would you want to ask the carrier representative and the dock workers?

4) If you declare the incident as being terminated and leave the scene, what liability would there be to you as the Safety Officer if the dock workers were injured? What could you recommend to reduce your liability?

SUMMARY AND REVIEW

1. There are five factors that should be evaluated by the IC in order to positively influence the outcome of an emergency. These can be remembered by the acronym MOTEL. Identify the factors:

   M – Magnitude

   O ____________

T – Timing

E – Effects

L ______________

2. The terms "strategy" and "tactics" are sometimes used interchangeably, but they actually have very different meanings. A strategy is a:
   a. Decision to take action
   b. Plan for managing resources
   c. Plan for visualizing outcomes
   d. Set of actions for achieving objectives

3. Common strategic goals implemented at hazmat incidents include rescue and public protective actions. Identify at least one other strategic goal:

4. Which of the following persons should NOT get involved in making detailed tactical-level decisions, like which type of plug to use:
   a. Incident Commander (IC)
   b. Hazmat Group Leader
   c. Group/Division Leader
   d. Sector Officer

5. Selecting the best strategic goal involves weighing what will be gained against the "costs" of what will be lost—a process often easier said than done. Determining what will be "gained" involves weighing many different variables, including potential casualties and fatalities. Identify at least one other variable:

6. High-angle rescue is one example of a technical hazmat rescue situation. Identify another technical hazmat rescue situation:

7. Confined spaces have a number of hazardous characteristics, including limited egress. Identify at least two other hazardous characteristics:

8. There are four important criteria that must be met before dilution is attempted. These include determining in advance that the substance is not water reactive. Identify at least two of the other criteria:

9. Why are containment tactics considered offensive operations?

10. The following are all pressure isolation and reduction tactics, except one:
    a. Flaring
    b. Vent and burn
    c. Vapor dispersion
    d. Hot tapping

11. Which of the following is the baseline for hazmat decision making and should be the element against which all strategies and tactics are compared:
    a. What are the physical and chemical properties of the material?
    b. What is the likelihood of the incident growing and involving other containers?
    c. Are specialized resources required?
    d. What will happen if I do nothing?

12. There are a number of size-up issues that must be addressed at flammable liquids emergencies, including the time the fire started, What other information will you want to have?

13. Under what conditions are offensive tactics implemented at flammable liquids fires:

14. With regard to tank firefighting, alcohol-resistant FFFP foam:
   a. Can be mixed with AFFF
   b. Should not be used with salt water
   c. Should only be applied to a polar solvent fuel
   d. Can be plunged into the fuel during application

15. True or False: Finished foams of a similar type but from different manufacturers (e.g., all AFFF's) are considered compatible.

16. With regard to cooling water for exposed tanks and pressure vessels, atmospheric storage tanks from 100 ft diameter to 150 ft diameter require _______ gallons of water per minute.

17. The most commonly encountered flammable gases are natural gas (i.e., methane or CH_4) and:

18. With regard to flammable gas emergencies, thermal stress is the primary concern in a fire situation; however, _______ stress may be an equal concern.

19. Tactical priorities for managing a flammable gas fire are to protect primary and secondary exposures to the fire and isolate the flammable gas source feeding the fire. Identify at least one additional tactical priority:

20. When a BLEVE is imminent, what is the best tactical strategy:

Nonintervention / Defensive tactics / Offensive tactics

21. BLEVEs of bulk containers and process vessels can produce severe fire and fragmentation risks within ____ feet of the failed container:
    a. 500
    b. 1000
    c. 1500
    d. 3000

22. Which of the following presents responders with the <u>fewest</u> tactical options:
    a. Reactive chemicals fires
    b. Flammable gas fires
    c. Flammable liquid fires

23. When dealing with large quantities of strong oxidizers and organic peroxides, responders should consider treating the incident like a(n) ________fire.
    a. Flammable gas
    b. Flammable liquids
    c. Explosives
    d. Radioactive materials

24. Before transferring site control to non-emergency response personnel, the IC should verify that any environmental spill contractors used for clean-up and recovery operations are trained per the requirements of.
    a. ANSI Z88.2—Practices for Respiratory Protection
    b. NFPA 471—Recommended Practice for Responding to Hazardous Material Incidents
    c. OSHA 1910.120 —Hazardous Waste Operations and Emergency Response
    d. OSHA Directive Number CPL 2-2/59A—Inspection Procedures for the Hazardous Waste Operations and Emergency Response Standard.

25. Identify at least one site safety consideration that should be addressed during product removal operation:

26. Of the three primary methods of liquid product transfer—gravity flow, pump transfer, and pressure transfer—which does NOT allow the use of vapor recovery:

27. Liquefied gases (MC-331 cargo tank trucks) and cryogenic liquids (MC-338 cargo tank trucks) may be transferred through the use of pumps, compressors and pressure differential. Which of these methods does NOT increase the internal pressure of the damaged tank:

28. Depending on their rating and design features, vacuum trucks can handle:
    a. Flammable and combustible liquids
    b. Corrosives
    c. Some poisons
    d. All of the above

29. True or False: NEVER upright a loaded aluminum-shell MC-306/DOT-406 cargo tank truck.

30. The decision to either (1) offload the contents and then upright the container, or (2) upright the container while still loaded will be dependent upon a number of variables, including the type of cargo tank truck involved. Identify at least one other variable that should be considered:

SUMMARY AND REVIEW ANSWER KEY

1.
   M – Magnitude
   O – Occurrence
   T – Timing
   E – Effects
   L – Location (p. 423)

2. b. Plan for managing resources (p.423)

3. To be correct, your answer should include at least one of the following:
   - Spill control (confinement)
   - Leak control (containment)
   - Fire control
   - Recovery (p. 424)

4. a. Incident Commander (IC) (p.425, 428)

5. To be correct, your answer should include at least one of the following:
   - Potential property damage or financial loss
   - Potential environmental damage
   - Potential disruption of the community (p. 426)

6. To be correct, your answer should include at least one of the following:
   - Victims pinned and trapped inside wreckage or debris
   - Confined space rescue situations (p. 430)

7. To be correct, your answer should include at least two of the following:
   - Hazardous atmospheres
   - Extended travel distances
   - Unusual physical hazards (such as being struck by falling objects)
   - Darkness
   - Poor Communications (p. 433)

8. To be correct, your answer should include at least two of the following:
   - Substance will not generate a toxic
   - Substance will not form any kind of solid or precipitate; and
   - Substance is totally water soluble (p. 438)

9. Containment tactics require personnel to enter the hot zone to control the release at its source and should be considered high-risk operations. (p. 442)

10. c. Vapor dispersion (p.451-453)

11. d. What will happen if I do nothing? (p.455)

12. To be correct, your answer should include at least two of the following:

    - Time at which responders arrived on scene.
    - Probability that the fire will be confined to its present size.
    - Fuel involved (flammable or combustible liquid), including the quantity, surface area involved, and the depth of the spill.
    - Hazards involved, including flash point, reactivity, solubility and specific gravity.
    - Estimated pre-burn time.
    - Layout of the incident, including the following specific points:
      - Type of storage tank(s) involved.
      - Size of the dike area(s) involved.
      - Valves and piping systems stressed or destroyed by the fire.
      - All surrounding exposures, including tanks, buildings, process units, utilities, and so on. (p. 458)

13. Offensive tactics are implemented when sufficient water and firefighting foam supplies and related resources are available for a continuous, uninterrupted fire attack. (p. 459)

14. d. Can be plunged into the fuel during application (p. 462)

15. True (p. 462)

16. 1,000 (p. 472)

17. Liquefied petroleum gas (propane or C_3H_8). (p. 472)

18. Mechanical (e.g., overturned cargo tank truck, derailed tank car) (p. 474)

19. To be correct, your answer should include at least one of the following:
    - Reduce the operating pressure of the line feeding the fire.
    - Permit the fire to self-extinguish and consume residual flammable gas inside the vessel or piping system.
    - Control and extinguish secondary fires. (p. 474)

20. Nonintervention (p. 474)

21. d. 3000 (p. 475)

22. a. Reactive chemicals fires (p. 481)

23. c. Explosives (p. 483)

24. c. OSHA 1910.120—Hazardous Waste Operations and Emergency Response (p. 484)

25. To be correct, your answer should include at least one of the following:
    - When flammable or combustible liquids are involved, ensure that backup crews with a minimum of two 1-3/4-inch foam handlines and at least one 20- to 30-pound dry chemical fire extinguisher are in place to protect all personnel involved in the offloading and uprighting operation.
    - Always have an escape plan with an alternate escape route.
    - Continuously monitor the hazard area for flammability, toxicity, and oxygen deficiency, as required by the hazards of the materials involved.
    - Ensure that all personnel remain alert (use rotation and rehab) (p. 485-486)

26. Pressure transfer (p. 490)

27. Pumps. (Under this method, the pressure between the damaged tank and the receiving tank are first equalized. A transfer pump is then used to move the contents into the receiving tank.) (p. 491)

28. d. All of the above (p. 492)

29. True (p. 495)

30. To be correct, your answer should include at least one of the following:
    - The nature of container
    - Stress and damage,
    - The location of the incident
    - Resources available to lift the damaged container (p. 495)

SELF EVALUATION

Please review all your work in this lesson. Now that you have completed this lesson, please take about 15 minutes to note your stronger and weaker areas.

Overall I feel I did (very well / well / fair / not so well) on the acronyms and abbreviations exercise.

Overall I feel I did (very well / well / fair / not so well) on the self-test questions.

Overall I feel I did (very well / well / fair / not so well) on the summary and review questions.

When compared to the previous lessons, I think I performed (better / worse / equally well).

List two areas in Chapter 10 in which you feel you could improve your skill or knowledge level:

1.

2.

Consider the following self-evaluation questions as they pertain to Chapter 10:

Am I taking effective margin notes?

Am I dedicating enough quality time to my studies?

Is anything distracting my focus?

Was any part of Chapter 10 too advanced for me?

Did I find that I don't have enough background experience to sufficiently grasp certain subject areas?

For areas in which I did particularly well, was it because I'm particularly interested in that subject matter? How so?

Were some things easier to learn because I have prior experience in learning or working with the concepts or principles?

Did I find that certain portions of the textbook seem to be better organized and effective in explaining key points?

What other Students have had to say about Chapter 10 material:

"Based on my lack of experience in major hazmat incidents, the containment and confinement tactics are challenging to learn.

It is evident to me that to succeed in a technical rescue under the pressure of a high-level hazmat incident, all involved must be well-trained and well-equipped and should have some degree of compatibility working together.

My hazmat team usually has a group discussion about goals and strategies to make sure that the hazmat officer hasn't overlooked something.

Transfer and recovery topics were a little difficult for me due to not having any experience with that phase of the incident.

These are the issues and considerations that are swirling around in the minds of the incident commander as he or she sits in the solitude of their command vehicle, that company level officers like me rarely get a glimpse of. I don't know what the future holds in store for me, but if I ever ascend to a position that includes this level of responsibility, this information will serve me well.

Making decisions about strategy and tactics is highly important to me as a hazmat technician and because I have a high potential in being the incident commander of a hazmat emergency in my volunteer department.

Selecting and evaluating response objectives to achieve strategic goals. That sentence alone sets my head a little dizzy."

Pat on the Back

Congratulations on working though Chapter 10 in the textbook and for completing the exercises in this lesson.

CHAPTER 11

DECONTAMINATION

CHAPTER ORIENTATION

Open the text to page 510. Take about 10 minutes to skim the chapter. Pay attention to the boldface subject headings. Read the titles to all the figures and note how they fit into the subject headings. Scan the case studies. Please read the introduction and summary sections carefully. When you have finished looking through Chapter 11, respond to the following items. Please use the textbook as you jot down your comments in the spaces provided below:

1. In your own words, what is the basis for the statement, "If you are good at decon, you will probably be good at preventing exposures."

2. Reflect on your current level of knowledge or background experience about the topics covered in Chapter 11. Where have you read about, learned about, or applied this knowledge in the past?

3. What sections or parts of Chapter 11 strike you as looking especially interesting?

4. What particular subjects in this chapter are important for a person in your position to master?

5. What do you predict will be the hardest things for you to learn in this chapter?

LEARNING OBJECTIVES

Turn to pages 510-511 and examine the chapter objectives. When you have finished, respond to the following question:

1. Which objectives in Chapter 11 do you feel you can achieve right now, with a reasonable level of confidence?

Highlight or place a check mark next to those objectives on pages 510-511 that addresses educational competencies referenced in *NFPA 472—Professional Competence of Responders to Hazardous Materials*.

As you read the sections of the chapter that deal with the objectives you have identified above, make sure your ideas or knowledge base match those of the authors. If not, you should examine how your current understanding of the material differs from that of the authors'. Depending on the level at which you wish to master the subject, discrepancies will have to be rectified and gaps will need to be filled.

ABBREVIATIONS AND ACRONYMS

The following abbreviations and acronyms are used in Chapter 11:

ALARA	As Low As Reasonably Achievable (p. 514, 526, 537)
APR	Air-Purifying Respirator (p. 530)
Decon	Decontamination (found on nearly every page in this chapter)
HEPA	High-Efficiency Particulate Air (p. 524)

mR	Milliroentgens (p. 520, 521)
NFPA	National Fire Protection (p. 512, 544)
PAPR	Powered Air Purifying Respirator (p. 530)
PERO	Post-Emergency Response Operations (p. 546)
PID	Photo Ionization Detectors (p. 527)
START	Simple Triage and Rapid Treatment Process (p. 541)
WMD	Weapons of Mass Destruction (p. 529, 541)

Locate these abbreviations and acronyms in the textbook (page numbers provided above) and underline them. Read the paragraph in which they are used.

ABBREVIATIONS AND ACRONYMS CROSSWORD

Use the clues below to solve the crossword.

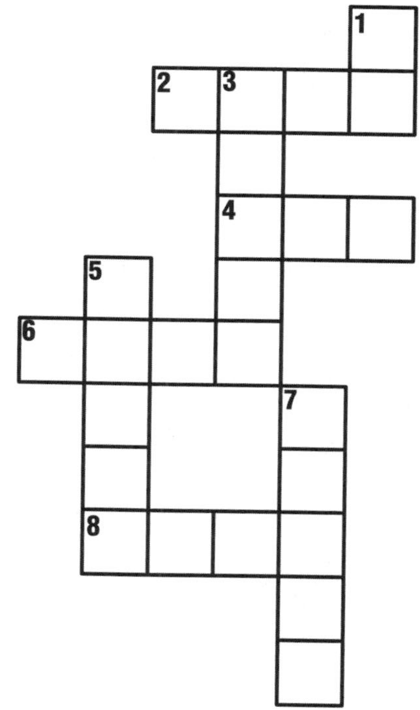

Across

2. These respirators use a blower to force the ambient air through air-purifying elements to a fullface mask.
4. These devices remove particulate matter, gases or vapors from the atmosphere.
6. These filters can capture particles as small as 0.1 microns.
8. This organization provides information on designing decon capability within a health care facility.

Down

1. A unit of radiation exposure
3. This principle is intended to ensure that most radiation exposures will be well below the defined limit.
5. The removal of hazardous substances from people and equipment to the extent necessary to preclude foreseeable health effects.
7. A method of triaging large numbers of patients at an emergency incident.

The Crossword Answer Key is at the end of this chapter.

STUDY SESSION OVERVIEW

Read pages 511 to the top of page 532, then take a short break to think about what you have read. Then read the rest of the chapter. Take margin notes as you go. Underline or highlight phrases that you feel are important.

When you have completed your reading, respond to the following questions. You may use the textbook to help you answer the questions, or work from memory.

1. At what point in the 8-step process must you begin considering decon methods and procedures?

2. Give an example that illustrates how a responder who has been contaminated while wearing PPE could also be exposed to the contaminant.

3. Explain the difference between surface contaminants and permeation contaminants. Provide an example of each.

4. Why are product specialists often the best source of decon information for public safety organizations?

5. Why should a contaminated victim's clothing should be removed directionally, from head to toe?

6. What considerations or concerns must be addressed during decon at a scene involving possible criminal activity?

SELF-TEST

Answer the following questions. You may use the textbook to help you answer the questions, or work from memory.

1. The scope, nature, and complexity of decon operations are defined by:
   [p. 512]
   a. The hazards and risks presented by the incident
   b. The type and level of protective clothing worn
   c. The decon equipment available
   d. The extent to which responders have been exposed

2. True or False: You cannot conduct safe entry operations if you have no way to perform decontamination.
   [p. 511]

3. The best method of decontamination is to:
   [p. 512]
   a. Avoid contamination
   b. Conduct all operations in the Hot Zone
   c. Begin clean-up operations as soon as possible
   d. Use disposable protective clothing

4. Which of the following terms is defined as the initial phase of the decontamination process during which the amount of surface contaminant is significantly reduced:
   [p. 513]
   a. Mass decontamination
   b. Direct decontamination
   c. Gross decontamination
   d. Primary decontamination

5. Emergency decontamination is the process of immediately reducing contamination of individuals in potentially life-threatening situations with or without:
   [p. 514]
   a. Standby medical assistance
   b. Standard decon procedures
   c. The acknowledgement of the Incident Commander
   d. The formal establishment of a decontamination corridor

6. Which of the following is an example of an exposure:
   [p. 514]
   a. A responder breathes toluene vapors but does not experience any symptoms
   b. A bystander gets gasoline on his hands
   c. A child swallows a small amount of mercury
   d. All of the above

7. Use the following words to complete the sentence below:
   exposure, decon, contaminant

If contact with the ________________ can be controlled, the risk of ________________ is reduced, and the need for ________________ can be minimized.
[p. 515]

8. True or False: Permeation can occur with any porous material, not just PPE.
[p. 516]

9. Cross contamination occurs when:
[p. 517]
   a. The contaminant is not completely removed from a material and continues to permeate through the material
   b. Any form of exposure occurs as a result of a breach or failure of PPE
   c. A person who is already contaminated makes contact with a person or object that is not contaminated
   d. A person who has been contaminated causes another person to become exposed

10. Mercury, ethylene dibromide (EDB), and benzene are all examples of:
[p. 518]
   a. Persistent contaminants
   b. Allergenic contaminants
   c. Reactive contaminants
   d. Moderate to highly chronic toxicity contaminants

11. Embryotoxic contaminants are also called:
[p. 518]
   a. Teratogens
   b. Nerve agents
   c. Poisons
   d. Tertiary hazards

12. Virulence is:
[p. 519]
   a. The speed at which viruses reproduce and spread
   b. The ability of the biological material to cause disease
   c. The degree to which viruses are resistant to antibodies
   d. Potential to cause damage to the human body as a result of a single exposure

13. The passage of ______ half-lives will bring a radiation level down to 1% of what it is at the time you take the first reading:
[p. 520]
   a. 2
   b. 4
   c. 7
   d. 10

Identify each of the decon methods below as either a physical method or a chemical method:
[p.522]

14. Physical Method / Chemical Method: Dilution

15. Physical Method / Chemical Method: Brushing and scraping

16. Physical Method / Chemical Method: Pressurized air

17. Physical Method / Chemical Method: Disinfection

18. Physical Method / Chemical Method: Adsorption

19. Physical Method / Chemical Method: Sterilization

20. Physical Method / Chemical Method: Washing

21. Physical Method / Chemical Method: Neutralization

22. Physical Method / Chemical Method: Solidification

23. Physical Method / Chemical Method: Evaporation

24. The following statements about absorption are all true, except one:
[p. 522]
   a. Absorbent materials should be inert
   b. Contaminants in absorbents remain chemically unchanged
   c. Absorption has universal and nearly boundless application for decontaminating personnel
   d. The most readily available absorbents are soil, diatomaceous earth, and vermiculite

25. The Decon Officer reports to the :
[p. 527]
   a. Incident Commander
   b. Safety Officer
   c. Hazmat Group Supervisor
   d. Entry Officer

26. The following statements about the decontamination corridor are all true, except one:
[p. 529, 539]
   a. The decon corridor should be clearly identified
   b. Only one decon corridor should be operating at a time
   c. The decon corridor begins in the Hot Zone and exits near the Warm Zone/Cold Zone interface
   d. Portable tents and specially designed vehicles or trailers may be integrated into the decon corridor

27. Which of the following persons <u>must</u> receive secondary decon:
[p. 533]
   a. Decon personnel
   b. Entry team members
   c. Patients requiring medical treatment
   d. Persons contaminated with flammable materials

28. During decon, which of the following should always be the last item removed: [p. 538]
   a. Gloves
   b. Boots
   c. Undergarments
   d. Respiratory protection

29. When dealing with large numbers of victims in a mass decon situation, which of the following is crucial and should be accomplished as soon as possible: [p. 540]
   a. Quick air monitoring and detection
   b. Establishment of the mass decon corridor
   c. Transportation all victims to medical facilities
   d. Separation of significantly contaminated individuals from those who may not be contaminated

30. Studies involving chemical warfare agents show that victims should be washed for at least 3 minutes but no longer than: [p. 540]
   a. 5 minutes
   b. 10 minutes
   c. 15 minutes
   d. 20 minutes

ANSWER KEY

Check your answers. If you missed more than six, you should read the chapter once again.

1. The scope, nature, and complexity of decon operations are defined by: [p. 512]
   a. The hazards and risks presented by the incident
   b. The type and level of protective clothing worn
   c. The decon equipment available
   d. The extent to which responders have been exposed

2. **True** or False: You cannot conduct safe entry operations if you have no way to perform decontamination. [p. 511]

3. The best method of decontamination is to: [p. 512]
   a. Avoid contamination
   b. Conduct all operations in the Hot Zone
   c. Begin clean-up operations as soon as possible
   d. Use disposable protective clothing

4. Which of the following terms is defined as the initial phase of the decontamination process during which the amount of surface contaminant is significantly reduced:

[p. 513]

a. Mass decontamination
b. Direct decontamination
c. Gross decontamination
d. Primary decontamination

5. Emergency decontamination is the process of immediately reducing contamination of individuals in potentially life-threatening situations with or without:
[p. 514]
a. Standby medical assistance
b. Standard decon procedures
c. The acknowledgement of the Incident Commander
d. The formal establishment of a decontamination corridor

6. Which of the following is an example of an exposure:
[p. 514]
a. A responder breathes toluene vapors but does not experience any symptoms
b. A bystander gets gasoline on his hands
c. A child swallows a small amount of mercury
d. All of the above

7. Use the following words to complete the sentence below:
exposure, decon, contaminant
If contact with the contaminant can be controlled, the risk of exposure is reduced, and the need for decon can be minimized. [p. 515]

8. **True** or False: Permeation can occur with any porous material, not just PPE.
[p. 516]

9. Cross contamination occurs when:
[p. 517]
a. The contaminant is not completely removed from a material and continues to permeate through the material
b. Any form of exposure occurs as a result of a breach or failure of PPE
c. A person who is already contaminated makes contact with a person or object that is not contaminated
d. A person who has been contaminated causes another person to become exposed

10. Mercury, ethylene dibromide (EDB), and benzene are all examples of:
[p. 518]
a. Persistent contaminants
b. Allergenic contaminants
c. Reactive contaminants
d. Moderate to highly chronic toxicity contaminants

11. Embryotoxic contaminants are also called:
[p. 518]
a. Teratogens
b. Nerve agents
c. Poisons
d. Tertiary hazards

12. Virulence is:
[p. 519]
a. The speed at which viruses reproduce and spread
b. The ability of the biological material to cause disease
c. The degree to which viruses are resistant to antibodies
d. Potential to cause damage to the human body as a result of a single exposure

13. The passage of ______ half-lives will bring a radiation level down to 1% of what it is at the time you take the first reading:
[p. 520]
a. 2
b. 4
c. 7
d. 10

Identify each of the decon methods below as either a physical method or a chemical method:
[p.522]

14. **Physical Method** / Chemical Method: Dilution

15. **Physical Method** / Chemical Method: Brushing and scraping

16. **Physical Method** / Chemical Method: Pressurized air

17. Physical Method / **Chemical Method**: Disinfection

18. **Physical Method** / Chemical Method: Adsorption

19. Physical Method / **Chemical Method**: Sterilization

20. **Physical Method** / Chemical Method: Washing

21. Physical Method / **Chemical Method**: Neutralization

22. Physical Method / **Chemical Method**: Solidification

23. **Physical Method** / Chemical Method: Evaporation

24. The following statements about absorption are all true, except one:
[p. 522]
a. Absorbent materials should be inert
b. Contaminants in absorbents remain chemically unchanged
c. Absorption has universal and nearly boundless application for decontaminating personnel
d. The most readily available absorbents are soil, diatomaceous earth, and vermiculite

25. The Decon Officer reports to the:
[p. 527]
a. Incident Commander
b. Safety Officer
c. Hazmat Group Supervisor
d. Entry Officer

26. The following statements about the decontamination corridor are all true, except one:
[p. 529, 539]
a. The decon corridor should be clearly identified
b. Only one decon corridor should be operating at a time
c. The decon corridor begins in the Hot Zone and exits near the Warm Zone/Cold Zone interface
d. Portable tents and specially designed vehicles or trailers may be integrated into the decon corridor

27. Which of the following persons must receive secondary decon:
[p. 533]
a. Decon personnel
b. Entry team members
c. Patients requiring medical treatment
d. Persons contaminated with flammable materials

28. During decon, which of the following should always be the last item removed:
[p. 538]
a. Gloves
b. Boots
c. Undergarments
d. Respiratory protection

29. When dealing with large numbers of victims in a mass decon situation, which of the following is crucial and should be accomplished as soon as possible:
[p. 540]
a. Quick air monitoring and detection
b. Establishment of the mass decon corridor
c. Transportation all victims to medical facilities
d. Separation of significantly contaminated individuals from those who may not be contaminated

30. Studies involving chemical warfare agents show that victims should be washed for at least 3 minutes but no longer than:
[p. 540]
a. 5 minutes
b. 10 minutes
c. 15 minutes
d. 20 minutes

PRACTICE

1. On page 518, the text advises us to always expect flammables and combustibles to present more than one contamination problem. Using outside resources, identify at least one secondary hazard and one tertiary hazard for each of the following: gasoline, acetone, benzene, and ethanol (liquids).

2. Arrange to visit a fixed facility in which hazmats will be found, such as a manufacturing facility. During your site visit, identify at least three fixed or engineered safety systems that may be found within such facilities (see page 544) and describe how each can facilitate the delivery of timely and effective decon.

3. Write an SOP or checklist for clean-up operations for decon of small and portable equipment, such as hand tools, fire hose, and monitoring equipment. Refer to page 546-547.

4. Write an SOP or checklist for clean-up/decon of motor vehicles and heavy equipment. Refer to pages 547-458.

5. Go to http://www.8stepprocess.com for additional information and activities pertaining to Chapter 11 "Decontamination."

IMPORTANT TERMINOLOGY

The following are all important terms that you should know in order to understand the materials in this chapter. Review these terms and definitions on page 513. Then compete the terminology exercise below:

Safe refuge area

Contaminant

Contamination
Decontamination
Decontamination corridor
Decontamination team
Degradation
Disinfection
Exposure
Sterilization

On the line next to each term in Column A, print the letter of its definition from Column B.

Column A Terminology	**Column B Definitions**
1._______Safe refuge area	A. The molecular breakdown of the spilled or released material to render it less hazardous.
2._______Contaminant	B. The physical and/or chemical process of reducing and preventing the spread of contamination from persons and equipment used at a hazardous materials incident.
3._______Contamination	C. The process of destroying all microorganisms in or on an object.
4._______Decontamination	D. Is managed by the Decon Leader and is responsible determining, implementing, and evaluating the decon procedure.
5._______Decontamination corridor	E. A hazardous material that physically remains on or in people or equipment, thereby creating a continuing risk of direct injury or a risk of exposure outside of the Hot Zone.
6._______Decontamination team	F. The process used to destroy the majority of recognized pathogenic microorganisms.
7._______Degradation	G. A distinct area within the Warm Zone that functions as a bridge between the Hot Zone and the Cold Zone, where decontamination stations are located.
8._______Disinfection	H. A temporary holding area for contaminated people until a decontamination corridor is set up.
9._______Exposure	I. The process of transferring a hazardous material from its source to people or equipment, which may act as a carrier.
10._______Sterilization	J. The process by which people and equipment are subjected to or come in contact with a hazardous material.

ANSWER KEY

Column A Terminology	Column B Definitions
1.__H__Safe refuge area	A. The molecular breakdown of the spilled or released material to render it less hazardous.
2.__E__Contaminant	B. The physical and/or chemical process of reducing and preventing the spread of contamination from persons and equipment used at a hazardous materials incident.
3.__I__Contamination	C. The process of destroying all microorganisms in or on an object.
4.__B__Decontamination	D. Is managed by the Decon Leader and is responsible determining, implementing, and evaluating the decon procedure.
5.__G__Decontamination corridor	E. A hazardous material that physically remains on or in people or equipment, thereby creating a continuing risk of direct injury or a risk of exposure outside of the Hot Zone.
6.__D__Decontamination team	F. The process used to destroy the majority of recognized pathogenic microorganisms.
7.__A__Degradation	G. A distinct area within the Warm Zone that functions as a bridge between the Hot Zone and the Cold Zone, where decontamination stations are located.
8.__F__Disinfection	H. A temporary holding area for contaminated people until a decontamination corridor is set up.
9.__J__Exposure	I. The process of transferring a hazardous material from its source to people or equipment, which may act as a carrier.
10.__C__Sterilization	J. The process by which people and equipment are subjected to or come in contact with a hazardous material.

STUDY GROUP ACTIVITY

1. Assume you are responding to an emergency that involves leaking drums of oleum. Set your own parameters for the incident, and then, working individually, each member of the group should list their decon method(s) and concerns. Then rejoin to discuss as a group. If time permits, repeat this activity substituting drums of magnesium phosphide for the oleum.

2. As a group, discuss and elaborate on the following statement found on page 519: "The fact that an area is contaminated with an etiologic does not necessary mean that a person has been exposed to, or is susceptible to the effects of an exposure."

STUDY GROUP LEARNING THOUGH INQUIRY SCENARIO 11-1

An Emergency Medical Technician (EMT) and Paramedic are staffing an EMS unit, which has been dispatched to a single family dwelling for a man suffering a heart attack. The individual is found in the basement slumped over a table. On the table and floor are several chemical containers, including several herbicides and sodium hypochlorite. The individual was known to "play with chemical mixtures" in his home, and was apparently in the process of developing a chemical formulation when he was stricken.

While handling the patient, both EMS personnel become unknowingly contaminated by some of the liquid product lying on the table. As the EMS personnel arrive at the hospital, they begin to experience a burning sensation on their arms and legs.

You are the Hazmat Officer and have been asked to respond to the hospital to provide technical advice. Although several emergency room personnel have received some hazardous materials training, the hospital has not yet developed a procedure for handling chemically contaminated patients and protecting their own personnel.

Based on the information provided and the information in Chapter 11, answer the following questions:

1) Has the patient been exposed or contaminated? (Review page 514.) What is the difference? Have the paramedics been exposed or contaminated? How could you tell the difference? How about the hospital workers? Have they been exposed or contaminated?

2) What options are available as to where the patient should be located? What are the pros and cons of each option?

3) How would you handle and treat both the chemically contaminated patient and EMS personnel? What precautions would you take to protect yourself during treatment?

4) Unfortunately, the patient dies shortly after his arrival at the hospital. Due to the unknown circumstances surrounding the incident, an autopsy is ordered. As the Hazmat Officer, you are asked to provide health and safety recommendations for conducting the autopsy to ensure that the hospital staff is properly protected during the estimated 2 hour event. What recommendations would you provide?

STUDY GROUP LEARNING THOUGH INQUIRY SCENARIO 11-2

You are the HMRT Officer at the scene of a hazmat incident involving a major poison gas release at a chemical process facility. A decision has been made to take immediate offensive action to close a valve that would stop the flow of gas. There is concern that the gas will drift downwind and go beyond the plant property and impact a nearby nursing home and medical facility.

A two-person entry team wearing chemical vapor protective clothing (EPA Level-A) enters the contaminated area to close the valve. Both HMRT members and the back-up crew have an internal suit radio communication capability.

The entry team locates the correct valve but needs a crowsfoot wrench to get the leverage they need to close the valve. Not having the proper wrench and running low on air, the Hazmat Safety Officer orders them out of the area to change out their air cylinders. As the entry team approaches the decontamination area, one member indicates by radio that he is experiencing a tingling situation in his fingers and toes. His voice is tense and he is clearly excited and breathing heavily. His partner is in control and is not experiencing any difficulties.

Based on the information that you have been provided and the information in Chapter 11, answer the following questions:

1) What could be the problem with the entry team member who is experiencing the tingling sensation in his fingers and toes? Of the potential problems, which you described, which ones are life threatening?

2) How would you handle the decontamination operation when the entry team arrives at the decon station? Does this situation justify an emergency decontamination? (Review page 534, Chapter 11.) If you conducted an emergency decon, what risks would there be to the entry team? What risks would there be to the decon team?

3) Assuming that you had a second team standing by for immediate entry with the crowsfoot wrench, would you permit them to enter the hazard area and close the valve while you are decontaminating the first entry team? If so, why? If not, why would you delay entry of the second team?

SUMMARY AND REVIEW

1. OSHA 1910.120 defines decontamination as the removal of hazardous substances from employees and their equipment to the extent necessary to:
   a. Eliminate all potential exposure
   b. Preclude foreseeable health effects
   c. Reduce the risk of exposure outside of the Hot Zone
   d. Make the hazardous material inert

2. Which of the following methods of decontamination is intended to immediately reduce contamination of a person in a potentially life-threatening situation with or without the formal establishment of a decontamination corridor:
   a. Technical decontamination
   b. Gross decontamination
   c. Physical decontamination
   d. Emergency decontamination

3. Which of the following types of decon are typically conducted at medical facilities:
   a. Mass decontamination
   b. Technical decontamination
   c. Radiological decontamination
   d. Cross-decontamination

4. Explain how each of the following factors can influence permeation:

   Contact time:

Concentration of the contaminant:

Temperature:

Physical state of the contaminant:

5. Which of the following is a water reactive contaminant:
   a. Magnesium phosphide
   b. Isocyanate
   c. Formamine
   d. Lewsite

6. Explain how "dose" influences an etiologic or biological material's ability to invade and alter the human body:

7. Which of the following is a limitation of dry decon:
   a. It must be preceded by brushing or scraping
   b. It can cause aerosolization of the contaminant into the surrounding atmosphere
   c. There is increased potential for cross-contamination
   d. It is not effective on petroleum-based materials

8. Which of the following is primarily used to decon equipment, vehicles, and structures that are contaminated with a corrosive material:
   a. Neutralization
   b. Dilution
   c. Evaporation
   d. Absorption

9. Is sterilization essentially the same as disinfection? If not, what is the difference?

10. Using visual observation, what are some indicators that decon is being effective or ineffective:

11. The Decon Officer normally performs all of the following activities, except one:
    a. Determines the appropriate level of decontamination to be provided
    b. Coordinates the transfer of decontaminated patients requiring medical treatment
    c. Monitors the effectiveness of decon operations
    d. Decontaminates all decon team personnel

12. Briefly describe an ideal outdoor decon site:

13. Identify at least one problem that can force the relocation of the decon area from its initial site:

14. The level of skin and respiratory protection required by Decon Team members will be dependent upon 1) the type of contaminants involved; 2) the level of contamination encountered by entry personnel; and 3):

15. Some online databases provide decon information. Identify at least three other sources for determining the appropriate decon methods:

16. Studies by the U.S. Army Soldier and Biological Chemical Command (SBCCOM) of nerve agent using harmless simulants to track contaminants have shown that approximately 80% of contaminants can be removed by:
   a. Undressing
   b. Washing with plain water
   c. Washing with water and detergent
   d. Wiping with isopropyl alcohol

17. What roles does law enforcement play in assisting with mass decon?

18. Information on designing decon capability within a health care facility can be found in:
   a. NFPA 58
   b. NFPA 70
   c. NFPA 99
   d. NFPA 473

19. What is the purpose of including water/sewage treatment facilities in the development for equipment decon plans?

20. Identify at least one special precaution that should be taken in the event that contaminated materials must remain at the incident scene until they can be removed for offsite cleaning or disposal:

SUMMARY AND REVIEW ANSWER KEY

1. b. Preclude foreseeable health effects (p. 513)

2. d. Emergency decontamination (p. 514)

3. b. Technical decontamination (p. 514)

4.
   - Contact time—The longer a contaminant is in contact with an object, the greater the probability and extent of permeation.

- Concentration—Molecules of the contaminant will flow from areas of high concentration to areas of low concentration. All things being equal, the greater the concentration of the contaminant, the greater the potential for permeation to occur.

- Temperature—Increased temperatures generally increase the rate of permeation. Conversely, lower temperatures will generally slow down the rate of permeation.

- Physical state—As a rule, gases, vapors, and low-viscosity liquids tend to permeate more readily than high viscosity liquids or solids. (p. 516)

5. a. Magnesium phosphide (p. 519)

6. Dose refers to the number of organisms that have been ingested, absorbed, or inhaled during an exposure period. The size, composition, and population of an etiologic will determine its ability to affect an exposed person. If an organism is not compatible with the host, or if there are not enough of the organisms to alter the natural balance within the human body, then the etiologic cannot survive, regardless of the dose. (p. 519-520)

7. c. There is increased potential for cross-contamination (p. 524)

8. a. Neutralization (p. 525)

9. Sterilization is not the same as disinfection. Sterilization is the process of destroying all microorganisms in or on an object. Disinfection results in a reduction in the number of viable organisms to some acceptable level. (p. 525-526)

10. Visual observation—Look for stains, discolorations, corrosive effects, and so on. (p. 527)

11. d. Decontaminates all decon team personnel (p. 528, 530)

12. The ideal outdoor decon site is upwind and uphill from the incident and remote from drains, manholes, and waterways, but close enough to the scene to limit the spread of contaminants. (p. 528)

13. Shifting winds, dispersing vapors (p. 528)

14. Where individuals are working along the decon line. The risk of heat exhaustion should also be factored in to decisionmaking when selecting the right PPE for decon. (p. 530)

15. To be correct, your answer should include at least three of the following:
    - Product specialists representing the chemical manufacturer
    - Technical information specialists with knowledge and understanding of the behavior and harm of the contaminants
    - Technical information centers, including CHEMTREC™, CANUTEC, SETIQ, Center for Disease Control, and regional poison control centers
    - Material safety data sheets (MSDS)
    - Emergency response guidebooks (p. 533)

16. a. Undressing (p. 534)

17. Law enforcement will play a key role in assisting with mass decon. Depending on the scenario, their training and expertise in controlling and containing large groups of people will be a major factor in a successful operation. More than a few people will want to leave the scene and seek medical treatment on their own, which defeats the goal of rapid decon. (p. 540)

18. c. NFPA 99 (p. 544)

19. Prior arrangements will be necessary before large quantities of waste water can be flushed into storm/sewer systems. As a rule, all waste should be contained until permission is received for disposal. (p. 546)

20. To be correct, your answer should include at least one of the following:
    - Take appropriate security measures. Always ensure that security is provided for hazardous waste and that the proper chain of custody is maintained.
    - Make sure appropriate warning signs are posted and labels are attached to containers. Additional lighting may be necessary when the materials remain overnight.
    - Make sure containers are properly sealed. (p. 548)

Crossword Answer Key:

Across
2. PAPR
4. APR
6. HEPA
8. NFPA

Down
1. mR
3. ALARA
5. Decon
7. START

SELF EVALUATION

Please review all your work in this lesson. Now that you have completed this lesson, please take about 15 minutes to note your stronger and weaker areas.

Overall I feel I did (very well / well / fair / not so well) on the acronyms and abbreviations exercise.

Overall I feel I did (very well / well / fair / not so well) on the self-test questions.

Overall I feel did (very well / well / fair / not so well) on the terminology exercise.

Overall I feel I did (very well / well / fair / not so well) on the summary and review questions.

When compared to the previous lessons, I think I performed (better / worse / equally well).

List two areas in Chapter 11 in which you feel you could improve your skill or knowledge level:

1.

2.

Consider the following self-evaluation questions as they pertain to Chapter 11:

Am I taking effective margin notes?

Am I dedicating enough quality time to my studies?

Is anything distracting my focus?

Was any part of Chapter 11 too advanced for me?

Did I find that I don't have enough background experience to sufficiently grasp certain subject areas?

For areas in which I did particularly well, was it because I'm particularly interested in that subject matter? How so?

Were some things easier to learn because I have prior experience in learning or working with the concepts or principles?

Did I find that certain portions of the textbook seem to be better organized and effective in explaining key points?

What other Students have had to say about Chapter 11 material:

"You have to be careful and remember lots of things when you decontaminate because it is the only permitted crossing point from the hot zone to the warm zone and if something contaminated gets by the decon area then your incident has just gotten bigger.

The distinctions between contamination and exposure were the hardest for me to follow. I guess I was complacent in my terminology; I used the terms interchangeably and am one of the individuals who confuse these two terms. I believe it is more of a mental error.

If decontamination is not taken seriously or is half done, many people can be at stake, such as family members, fellow employees and civilians, from materials, which were not taken off of the entry personnel.

Since I am the lieutenant in charge of the engine company for the department I could be placed in a position to be in charge of decontamination for a hazardous materials incident so decontamination is an important subject area for me to master.

Many times rank is not applicable to a hazmat, there are not enough officers to staff all the necessary command positions, so firefighters need to be able to plug in and function as supervisors. Decontamination is one of those functions that firefighters must master. Decon can take vast resources to establish, and must be done prior to any entry."

Pat on the Back

Congratulations on working though Chapter 11 in the textbook and for completing the exercises in this lesson.

CHAPTER 12
TERMINATING THE INCIDENT

CHAPTER ORIENTATION

Open the text to page 556. Take about 10 minutes to skim the chapter. Pay attention to the boldface subject headings. Read the titles to all the figures and note how they fit into the subject headings. Scan the case studies. Please read the introduction and summary sections carefully. When you have finished looking through Chapter 12, respond to the following items. Please use the textbook as you jot down your comments in the spaces provided below:

1. In your own words, how does a properly terminated hazmat incident help to ensure scene safety?

2. Reflect on your current level of knowledge or background experience about the topics covered in Chapter 12. Where have you read about, learned about, or applied this knowledge in the past?

3. What sections or parts of Chapter 12 strike you as looking especially interesting?

4. What particular subjects in this chapter are important for a person in your position to master?

5. What do you predict will be the hardest things for you to learn in this chapter?

LEARNING OBJECTIVES

Turn to page 556 and examine the chapter objectives. When you have finished, respond to the following question:

1. Which objectives in Chapter 12 do you feel you can achieve right now, with a reasonable level of confidence?

Highlight or place a check mark next to those objectives on page 556 that addresses educational competencies referenced in *NFPA 472—Professional Competence of Responders to Hazardous Materials*.

As you read the sections of the chapter that deal with the objectives you have identified above, make sure your ideas or knowledge base match those of the authors. If not, you should examine how your current understanding of the material differs from that of the authors'. Depending on the level at which you wish to master the subject, discrepancies will have to be rectified and gaps will need to be filled.

ABBREVIATIONS AND ACRONYMS

The following abbreviations and acronyms are used in Chapter 12:

IC	Incident Commander (p. 559, 560)
NFIRS	National Fire Incident Reporting System (p. 563)
PIA	Post Incident Analysis (p. 561, 562, 563)

PERO	Post-Emergency Response Operations (p. 557, 558, 559)
SOP	Standard Operating Procedures (p. 561, 569)

Locate these abbreviations and acronyms in the textbook (page numbers provided above) and underline them. Read the paragraph in which they are used.

EXERCISE:

Each of the abbreviations and acronyms listed above are used in the sentences below. Some sentences are true statements; others are false. For each sentence, indicate whether it is true or false:

1. True / False: The requirements of the OSHA Hazwoper regulation (29 CFR 1910.120) clearly delineate between the emergency phase of an incident response and the PERO.
[p. 558]

2. True / False: The IC should ensure that response operations are fully coordinated with law enforcement or investigation agencies involved in the incident.
[p. 559]

3. True / False: The PERO Incident Commander may be a contractor.
[p. 558]

4. True / False: The Safety Officer is responsible for transferring command to the PERO Incident Commander.
[p. 559]

5. True / False: The IC is nearly always the best facilitator for the debriefing.
[p. 560]

6. True / False: The PIA assures that the incident has been properly documented.
[p. 561]

7. True / False: The PIA should not be released to outside agencies.
[p. 561]

8. True / False: Most major public fire departments participate in the NFIRS.
[p. 563]

9. True / False: NFIRS is sponsored by the National Fire Protection Association.
[p. 563]

10. True / False: Liability problems can occur when written SOPs are not followed in the field.
[p. 569]

ANSWER KEY

1. **True** / False: The requirements of the OSHA Hazwoper regulation (29 CFR 1910.120) clearly delineate between the emergency phase of an incident response and the PERO. [p. 558]

2. **True** / False: The IC should ensure that response operations are fully coordinated with law enforcement or investigation agencies involved in the incident. [p. 559]

3. **True** / False: The PERO Incident Commander may be a contractor. [p. 558]

4. True / **False**: The Safety Officer is responsible for transferring command to the PERO Incident Commander. [p. 559]

5. True / **False**: The IC is nearly always the best facilitator for the debriefing. [p. 560]

6. **True** / False: The PIA assures that the incident has been properly documented. [p. 561]

7. True / **False**: The PIA should not be released to outside agencies. [p. 561]

8. **True** / False: Most major public fire departments participate in the NFIRS. [p. 563]

9. True / **False**: NFIRS is sponsored by the National Fire Protection Association. [p. 563]

10. **True** / False: Liability problems can occur when written SOPs are not followed in the field. [p. 569]

STUDY SESSION OVERVIEW

Read pages 557 to the top of page 566, then take a short break to think about what you have read. Then read the rest of the chapter. Take margin notes as you go. Underline or highlight phrases that you feel are important. When you have completed your reading, respond to the following questions. You may use the textbook to help you answer the questions, or work from memory.

1. Provide several examples of how scene safety can deteriorate when an incident transitions from its emergency phase to the restoration and recovery phase.

2. What key consideration determines if you should still be operating in the emergency response mode, or it is time to transition to the restoration and recovery phase.

3. Termination involves three principle phases. What are they and in what order should they take place?

4. From memory, list at least 5 sources of factual information about a response that would be collected in developing the Post incident analysis. Compare your list to the suggested sources of information on page 562.

5. Would you make a good critique leader? Why or why not?

SELF-TEST

Answer the following questions. You may use the textbook to help you answer the questions, or work from memory.

1. The following statements about termination are all true, except one:
   [p. 557]
   a. Termination is the final step in the Eight Step Incident Management Process
   b. Termination is the transition between the conclusion of emergency phase operations and the initiation of decontamination

c. Terminating the incident includes conducting a debriefing, post-incident analysis, and the incident critique
d. Termination includes the transfer of on-scene command from the IC to the individual responsible for managing the post-emergency response operations

2. Which of the following would be identified in an effective debriefing:
[p. 559]
a. The need for a critique
b. The need for more advanced training
c. Poor or inadequate cooperation among responders
d. Damaged equipment requiring servicing

3. The need for a Critical Incident Stress Debriefing is accessed during the:
[p. 560]
a. Debriefing
b. Incident notification
c. Post-Incident Analysis
d. Critique

4. Ideally, debriefings should take place:
[p. 560]
a. After the critique
b. After the incident has been properly documented and reported to the right regulatory agencies
c. As soon as the emergency phase of the operation is completed
d. As soon as the post-emergency response operations are concluded

5. Which of the following topics should be addressed <u>first</u> during the debriefing:
[p. 560]
a. Health information
b. Potential legal issues
c. Assignment of a follow-up contact person
d. Assignment of a critique leader

6. The Post-Incident Analysis is conducted to:
[p. 561]
a. Meet National Fire Incident Reporting System requirements
b. Gather necessary information for the debriefing
c. Prevent documentation of potentially damaging information
d. Assure that the incident has been properly documented and reported to the right regulatory agencies

7. The Post-Incident Analysis Coordinator:
[p. 561, 563]
a. Is usually appointed during the on-scene debriefing
b. Has the authority to determine who will have access to information
c. Cooperates with other official investigators to reconstruct the incident completely
d. All of the above

8. The rough draft PIA report should be reviewed by ________________ to verify that the available facts are arranged properly and actually took place:

[p. 563]

a. PIA Coordinator
b. Incident Commander
c. Key responders
d. Official investigators

9. Under CERCLA, the responsible party must report to the ______________ any spill or release of a specified hazardous substance in an amount equal to or greater than the reportable quantity (RQ) specified by EPA:
[p. 563]
   a. State Emergency Response Commission (SERC)
   b. National Fire Incident Reporting System (NFIRS)
   c. National Response Center (NRC)
   d. Occupational Safety and Health Administration (OSHA)

10. The primary purpose of a critique is to:
[p. 566]
   a. Comply with OSHA requirements
   b. Develop recommendations for improving the emergency response system
   c. Develop a chronological review of who did what, when, and where during the incident
   d. Provide a foundation for the development of formal investigations, which are usually conducted to establish the probable cause of the accident

11. Which of the following statements about the critique process is true:
[p. 566]
   a. The Safety Officer should always lead the critique
   b. Never use a critique to assign blame
   c. Critiques that are longer than 15 minutes are probably too long
   d. Critique reports are normally confidential and should not be released to the public

ANSWER KEY

Check your answers. If you missed more than two, you should read the chapter once again.

1. The following statements about termination are all true, except one:
[p. 557]
   a. Termination is the final step in the Eight Step Incident Management Process
   b. Termination is the transition between the conclusion of emergency phase operations and the initiation of decontamination
   c. Terminating the incident includes conducting a debriefing, post-incident analysis, and the incident critique
   d. Termination includes the transfer of on-scene command from the IC to the individual responsible for managing the post-emergency response operations

2. Which of the following would be identified in an effective debriefing:
[p. 559]
   a. The need for a critique
   b. The need for more advanced training
   c. Poor or inadequate cooperation among responders

d. Damaged equipment requiring servicing

3. The need for a Critical Incident Stress Debriefing is accessed during the:
   [p. 560]
   a. Debriefing
   b. Incident notification
   c. Post-Incident Analysis
   d. Critique

4. Ideally, debriefings should take place:
   [p. 560]
   a. After the critique
   b. After the incident has been properly documented and reported to the right regulatory agencies
   c. As soon as the emergency phase of the operation is completed
   d. As soon as the post-emergency response operations are concluded

5. Which of the following topics should be addressed first during the debriefing:
   [p. 560]
   a. Health information
   b. Potential legal issues
   c. Assignment of a follow-up contact person
   d. Assignment of a critique leader

6. The Post-Incident Analysis is conducted to:
   [p. 561]
   a. Meet National Fire Incident Reporting System requirements
   b. Gather necessary information for the debriefing
   c. Prevent documentation of potentially damaging information
   d. Assure that the incident has been properly documented and reported to the right regulatory agencies

7. The Post-Incident Analysis Coordinator:
   [p. 561, 563]
   a. Is usually appointed during the on-scene debriefing
   b. Has the authority to determine who will have access to information
   c. Cooperates with other official investigators to reconstruct the incident completely
   d. All of the above

8. The rough draft PIA report should be reviewed by ______________ to verify that the available facts are arranged properly and actually took place:
   [p. 563]
   a. PIA Coordinator
   b. Incident Commander
   c. Key responders
   d. Official investigators

9. Under CERCLA, the responsible party must report to the ______________ any spill or release of a specified hazardous substance in an amount equal to or greater than the reportable quantity (RQ) specified by EPA:

[p. 563]

a. State Emergency Response Commission (SERC)
b. National Fire Incident Reporting System (NFIRS)
c. National Response Center (NRC)
d. Occupational Safety and Health Administration (OSHA)

10. The primary purpose of a critique is to:
[p. 566]
a. Comply with OSHA requirements
b. Develop recommendations for improving the emergency response system
c. Develop a chronological review of who did what, when, and where during the incident
d. Provide a foundation for the development of formal investigations, which are usually conducted to establish the probable cause of the accident

11. Which of the following statements about the critique process is true:
[p. 566]
a. The Safety Officer should always lead the critique
b. Never use a critique to assign blame
c. Critiques that are longer than 15 minutes are probably too long
d. Critique reports are normally confidential and should not be released to the public

PRACTICE

1. Develop a checklist that could be used by the on-scene IC when formally transferring command to the PERO Incident Commander.

2. Write a letter addressed to a potential critique leader outside the response organization that briefly explains the critique process and outlines the role and duties of a critique leader.

3. Go to the form on pages 565. What does "Section 304" reporting" refer to? Go the EPA website and answer the following questions:
   - Who is responsible for reporting releases and when must the report be made?
   - What facilities are covered under EPCRA release reporting requirements?
   - What is the Section 304 EHS RQ for:

   Ethylene oxide _________

   Phosgene _________

   Amiton _________

   Diphacinone _________

   Trichloroactyl chloride _________

4. Browse the NFRS webpages on the USFA Web site (www.usfa.fema.gov). Who is your state's Point of Contact (POC)?

5. Go to http://www.8stepprocess.com for additional information and activities pertaining to Chapter 12 "Terminating the Incident."

STUDY GROUP ACTIVITY

1. Divide into two groups. One group is to develop a checklist for conducting a debriefing and the other group is to develop a checklist for conducting a critique. Rejoin as a larger group to compare and discuss the differences in the two checklists.

2. Assume that you, as a group, will be participating in a critique in which a major confrontation among the players is anticipated. Discuss and decide on a strategy for diffusing the problem as much as possible before the actual critique session takes place.

STUDY GROUP LEARNING THROUGH INQUIRY SCENARIO 12-1

You are the Safety Officer at a confined spaces incident that involved two contractors who died while attempting to clean sludge out of the bottom of an ethylene dibromide (EDB) tank. The first worker entered the tank without respiratory protection and was immediately overcome. The second worker crawled through the manway without respiratory protection to rescue his partner. He was also overcome by the EDB. When rescue personnel arrived on the scene five minutes later, they determined that the workers were discovered missing at lunch. A coworker was sent to investigate and found both men trapped in the tank.

When it became obvious that the workers had been trapped for several hours before the 911 call was placed, the Incident Commander stopped rescue operations and treated the incident as a body recovery operation. A confined spaces rescue team conducted the body recovery operation without any unusual problems. The Incident Commander has asked you to coordinate the termination phase of the incident and conduct an on-site debriefing of fire and rescue personnel. He reminds you that ethylene dibromide is a bad actor and a known carcinogen. He wants to make sure that the incident is terminated correctly with the proper documentation.

Based on the information that you have been provided and the information in Chapter 12, answer the following questions:

1) What post-incident safety and health concerns do you have that need to be worked into the debriefing? (Review page 559–561, Chapter 12.)

2) How long do you think it will take to conduct a debriefing that will adequately cover all of the points that you will need to make? Where would you conduct the debriefing and who should attend? Considering the potential health effects of EDB, what are your thoughts on the need for a follow-up medical evaluation? Would you conduct a critical incident stress debriefing? Why or Why not?

3) How would you handle a question from a member of the confined spaces rescue team if he stated that he knew that EDB was a strong poison but he did not realize during the pre-entry safety briefing that it was carcinogenic? He specifically wants to know whether the rescue team should go to the hospital for a follow-up medical examination.

STUDY GROUP LEARNING THROUGH INQUIRY SCENARIO 12-2

Your organization has traditionally conducted formal critiques of major incidents, although many of the personnel feel that the critiques have been inadequate and often "gloss over" critical problems and issues which have occurred. After attending a local Safety Symposium, which featured a workshop on critiquing techniques, you have the opportunity to brief your supervisor on your concerns with the current critique system. During the discussion you express your opinion that the manner by which critiques are conducted and findings and recommendations are developed, managed, and tracked are not very effective. In short, you tell your manager that the current critique process stinks and that the overall emergency response system is not being improved as a result of the critiques.

After hearing your viewpoints, your supervisor replies, "If you think the system is so bad, you develop a proposal to fix it!" You now have the opportunity you have been waiting for. Using the background information provided and the information discussed in Chapter 12 answer the following questions:

1) What should the primary emphasis of your critique program be? Why? (Review pages 566 to 567, Chapter 12.)

2) Considering your dissatisfaction with the existing critique program, whom would you recommend as the best type of critique facilitator? For example, should the critique facilitator come from the safety department, internal to your organization or external, etc.

3) How do you propose to document and distribute the lessons learned from the critiques throughout the organization?

4) How should follow-up items be tracked? How would you handle a situation where a particular supervisor doesn't believe in the critique system and simply throws away the critique reports and fails to share them with his subordinates?

SUMMARY AND REVIEW

1. When the IC terminates the emergency response phase and formally transfers command to the PERO Incident Commander, the IC should conduct a transfer briefing that covers the nature of the emergence and actions taken to stabilize and resolve the emergency. Identify at least two other matters that should be covered in the briefing:

2. There are many agencies and individuals who have a legitimate need for information about significant hazmat incidents, such as shipping representatives. Identify at least two other groups that have a legitimate need for information:

3. The Post Incident Analysis (PIA) is the reconstruction of the incident to establish a clear picture of the events that took place during the emergency. It is conducted to assure that the incident has been properly documented and reported to the right regulatory agencies. Identify at least one other reason why a PIA is conducted:

4. The PIA should focus on six key topics, listed below. For each topic, identify the key questions that should be answered by the PIA:

Example:

- **Command and control**: Was the Incident Management System established and was the emergency response organized according to the existing Emergency Response Plan and/or SOPs? Did information pass from Section personnel to the Incident Commander or through appropriate channels? Were response objectives clearly communicated to field personnel at the task level?

- **Tactical operations:**

- **Resources**:

- **Support Services**:

- **Plans and Procedures**:

- **Training**:

5. Listed below are five primary reasons for liability problems in emergency response work. They are worth considering as a case for building a strong critique program. Identify issues associated with each.

Example:

- **Problems with planning**: Plans and procedures are poorly written, out-of-date, and unrealistic. In addition, what is written in the SOP is not followed in the field.

- **Problems with training**:

- **Problems with identification of hazards**:

- **Problems with duty to warn**:

- **Problems with negligent operations**:

6. The following statements are pertain to either debriefings or critiques. Next to each statement, indicate whether it primarily pertains to a debriefing or a critique:

   a) Debriefing / Critique: The single most important way for an organization to self-improve over time.

   b) Debriefing / Critique: Assigns information gathering responsibilities for a post-incident analysis.

   c) Debriefing / Critique: OSHA requires that one be conducted of every hazardous materials emergency response.

   d) Debriefing / Critique: Should begin as soon as the emergency phase of the operation is completed.

   e) Debriefing / Critique: Inform responders exactly what hazmats they were (potentially) exposed to and their signs and symptoms.

   f) Debriefing / Critique: Identify unsafe site conditions that will impact the clean-up and recovery phase.

   g) Debriefing / Critique: The primary purpose of one is to develop recommendations for improving the emergency response system.

   h) Debriefing / Critique: Shares information among emergency response organizations.

   i) Debriefing / Critique: Should last no longer than 15 minutes.

   j) Debriefing / Critique: Has a published agenda.

   k) Debriefing / Critique: Is followed up with a short report.

   l) Debriefing / Critique: Promotes emergency response operations that are system-dependent rather than people-dependent organization.

SUMMARY AND REVIEW ANSWER KEY

1. To be correct, your answer should include two or more of the following:
   - Names of hazardous materials involved
   - Hazards and risks that were mitigated and those that still exist
   - Safety procedures
   - Relevant documentation
   - Points of contact (p. 559)

2. To be correct, your answer should include two or more of the following:
   - Manufacturing representatives
   - Carrier representatives
   - Insurance companies
   - Government agencies
   - Citizens groups (p. 561)

3. To be correct, your answer should include at least one of the following:
   - Determine the level of financial responsibility (i.e., who pays?).
   - Establish a clear picture of the emergency response for further study. Focus on the General Hazardous Materials Behavior Model. (See Chapter 8.)
   - Provide a foundation for the development of formal investigations, which are usually conducted to establish the probable cause of the accident for administrative, civil, or criminal proceedings.

4. To be correct, your answer should include at least one question from the following:
   - **Tactical operations**: Were tactical operations completed in a safe and effective manner? What worked? What did not? Were tactical operations conducted in a timely and coordinated fashion? Do revisions need to be made to tactical procedures or worksheets? (p. 562)
   - **Resources**: Were resources adequate to conduct the response effort? Are improvements needed to equipment or facilities? Were mutual aid agreements implemented effectively? (p. 562)
   - **Support Services**: Were support services adequate and provided in a timely manner? What is needed to increase the provision of support to the necessary level? (p. 562)
   - **Plans and Procedures**: Were the Emergency Response Plan and associated Tactical Procedures current? Did they adequately cover notification, assessment, response, recovery, and termination? Were roles and assignments clearly defined? How will plans and procedures be upgraded to reflect the "lessons learned"? (p. 562)
   - **Training**: Did this event highlight the need for additional basic or advanced training? Multi-agency training? Were personnel trained adequately for their assignments? (p. 562)

5. To be correct, your answer should include at least one issue from the following:

- **Problems with training.** No training is conducted, training evolutions reinforce unsafe practices, and the training is undocumented. (p. 569)
- **Problems with identification of hazards.** Hazards were not identified, were not prioritized, or were ignored even though they were known to exist. (p. 569)
- **Problems with duty to warn.** Warnings concerning safety hazards and design limitations of equipment were not given or were improper. (p. 569)
- **Problems with negligent operations.** Equipment was not employed properly, plans and procedures were not followed, and equipment was not maintained to an acceptable standard. (p. 569)

6.

a) Debriefing / **Critique**: The single most important way for an organization to self-improve over time. (p. 566)

b) **Debriefing** / Critique: Assigns information gathering responsibilities for a post-incident analysis. (p. 560)

c) Debriefing / **Critique**: OSHA requires that one be conducted of every hazardous materials emergency response. (p. 566)

d) **Debriefing** / Critique: Should begin as soon as the emergency phase of the operation is completed. (p. 560)

e) **Debriefing** / Critique: Inform responders exactly what hazmats they were (potentially) exposed to and their signs and symptoms. (p. 559)

f) **Debriefing** / Critique: Identify unsafe site conditions that will impact the clean-up and recovery phase. (p. 559)

g) Debriefing / **Critique**: The primary purpose of one is to develop recommendations for improving the emergency response system. (p. 566)

h) Debriefing / **Critique**: Shares information among emergency response organizations. (p. 566)

i) **Debriefing** / Critique: Should last no longer than 15 minutes (p, 560)

j) Debriefing / **Critique**: Has a published agenda. (p. 566)

k) Debriefing / **Critique**: Is followed up with a short report. (p. 567)

l) Debriefing / **Critique**: Promotes emergency response operations that are system-dependent rather than people-dependent organization. (p. 566)

SELF EVALUATION

Please review all your work in this lesson. Now that you have completed this lesson, please take about 15 minutes to note your stronger and weaker areas.

Overall I feel I did (very well / well / fair / not so well) on the acronyms and abbreviations exercise.

Overall I feel I did (very well / well / fair / not so well) on the self-test questions.

Overall I feel I did (very well / well / fair / not so well) on the summary and review questions.

When compared to the previous lessons, I think I performed (better / worse / equally well).

List two areas in Chapter 12 in which you feel you could improve your skill or knowledge level:

1.

2.

Consider the following self-evaluation questions as they pertain to Chapter 12:

Am I taking effective margin notes?

Am I dedicating enough quality time to my studies?

Is anything distracting my focus?

Was any part of Chapter 12 too advanced for me?

Did I find that I don't have enough background experience to sufficiently grasp certain subject areas?

For areas in which I did particularly well, was it because I'm particularly interested in that subject matter? How so?

Were some things easier to learn because I have prior experience in learning or working with the concepts or principles?

Did I find that certain portions of the textbook seem to be better organized and effective in explaining key points?

What other Students have had to say about Chapter 12 material:

"One area that is confusing for me is the difference between a critique and post-incident analysis. I always thought the two terms were interchangeable."

"I think that terminating the incident would be the hardest job for me, because there is always that thought in the back of your mind —-is there something I left out? Is there any more that I can do? These are the questions that can haunt you, especially if something is found to be wrong. Then legal matters may be involved."

"Successfully terminating the incident is more difficult to implement than I had originally thought. This is the most difficult and crucial part of the process nearing the end."

"While not necessarily difficult to follow, the termination phase is what I as a firefighter have the least experience with. By the time the incident is winding down Chief officers have usually arrived and assumed most command functions. I have been to critiques and debriefings, and have even presented them if I held a command position. But usually this is where we fail as a team, sometimes by the end of the incident everyone just wants to go home and the officers don't really see the need for this phase of the incident. Because of this I feel it's my weakest part of the process."

Pat on the Back

Congratulations on working though Chapter 12 in the textbook and for completing the exercises in this lesson.

NOTES

NOTES